This book is dedicated
to the memory of my
beautiful daughter
Heather

Combines in Camera

Sue Morgan

Best wishes
Sue Morgan
April 2013

Japonica Press

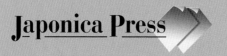

First Published 2010

ISBN: 978-1-904686-20-0

A catalogue record for this book is
available from the British Library

Published by

Japonica Press
Low Green Farm, Hutton,
Driffield, East Yorkshire,
United Kingdom, YO25 9PX

Sue Morgan - the author

Acknowledgements

I would like to thank everyone who has enabled me to produce this book by allowing me to take photographs:

Ray Turner of Morris Corfield, Benthall who suggestsed four years ago that I produce a book from my photographs of combines.

The directors and staff of **Morris Corfield** and Co Ltd., Benthall, Broseley, Shropshire.

Dave Harris

CLAAS KGaA mbH, Harsewinkel, Germany

Steve Mitchell, ASM Public Relations Ltd.

John Deere Ltd., Langar, Nottingham

Ravenhill Ltd., Hereford

Ron Knight, Great Casterton

Alexander and Duncan, Leominster

Alan Johnson, Tarleton, Southport

The Author

The Author was born in Much Wenlock, Shropshire and spent her childhood years in South Shropshire at the time when self propelled combines first appeared. The red MH and MF combines in the 1950's and 1960's dominated the harvest fields around her native village of Wistanstow, where she watched them at work for hours, firstly the 780 bagger machines and then the tanker versions, before the MF 400 and 500's came. Mixed with these were a few Claas Matadors and Allis-Chalmers Gleaners.

The Author's early fascination with farm machinery, in particular combines, was coupled with an interest in photography which began with a Brownie Box camera which she had inherited when she was 8 years old, before progressing to a Kodak Instamatic 104 which she received for her 12th birthday, so her interest in farm machinery photography began.

Many of her photographs feature combines from Claas and New Holland. Leon Claeys and August Claas were two of the most influential people in the development of the European combine. The Claeys MZ was closely followed by the Claas Hercules, renamed SF which both used the layout common to most European combines, grain tank behind driver followed by the engine. However this design was first used by a US manufacturer, John Deere on their model 55, and whose combines cut more grain worldwide than any other manufacturer. The author has included a selection of photographs to show the combines from this company over the decades in Britain. Many other combine manufactures appeared in the UK after the MH 780, including Ransomes of Ipswich have now long since gone, and imports from the US and from Europe such as Fahr, Activ and B M Volvo were seen in the harvest fields.

She left Shropshire for a time to attend boarding school in Malvern and North Wales, but on returning home for the summer holidays, she would see combines at work. The Author later returned home and went to Ludlow grammar school, and became involved with the young farmers movement and the farming community. Much of her time was spent on a local farm in her native village where she learnt to drive a Claas Senator.

She undertook a management course at Cardiff University and eventually left Shropshire when she married a dairy farmer on the Welsh borders, where bringing up two daughters and milking cows twice daily took over her activities for 18 years. When her daughters left home, with time on her hands her interest in and enthusiasm for combines was reawakened. She now lives on a mixed farm in Herefordshire.

Two years ago, the Author had an idea of forming a chronicle of British combine photographs, some of these older models from companies no longer in existence are still used to cut a few acres, and in this book she has been able to capture these on camera as a record for a future generation, together with some information about the companies which made them. Pictures include MH 780's, which were once often seen two or three in a field in the 1960's, to the 8-14ft cut 10 tonnes an hour models of the 1970's and the lone giant 40ft cut harvesters of today with upwards of 80 tonnes an hour capacity working in fields of a hundred hectares or more in size.

She has maintained a combined interest in farm machinery and photography, and writes occasional articles for magazines about machinery factories and produces a calendar featuring her photographs each year in aid of Macmillan Cancer Support. The Author has a collection of over a hundred combine scale models, a comprehensive collection of combine sales literature and a collection of Claas combines including a Senator 70, Consul, Standard Matador, Mercury and Europa. She has been a lifelong Claas fan, hence many of her photographs feature Claas combines, which epitomise German engineering at its best and together with New Holland now make up the largest proportion of combines seen in the British harvest fields of today.

Her website can be visited at www.sue-morganagrifotos.co.uk, where you can see more of her tractor and machinery photographs. She hopes you enjoy looking at this chronicle of combine photographs as much as she has enjoyed taking them. All photographs in this book are her own.

Contents

Intro

Part 1

Part 2

Introduction

The advent of the combine harvester revolutionised farming more than any other invention. For centuries, harvesting has been undertaken with sickle or scythe. Threshing was a separate operation. Then binders and threshing machines came along. Their arrival in Britain was slow in coming, compared to the American Midwest, Canada and Australia. The first combines were made in America in the 1830's. Hiram Moore invented his 'Michigan' combine, in the 1830s, this development continued with horse drawn machines which were later powered by steam engines and tractors. More than eight decades ago, three Kansas brothers first thought "why don't we bring the thresher to the crop rather than vice-versa?" and hit upon the world's first self-propelled combine, the Gleaner. By 1900, teams of horses and mules pulled combines and some were steam driven, but these did not appear in Europe until the late 1920's. George Berry designed a 40ft cut combine in the 1880's, which was steam powered. By 1940, the combine was well established in North America, but few were used on British farms, where the binder and threshing drum still dominated the harvest scene. The tractor had largely replaced the traction engine as the power source for threshing equipment, but horses were still seen pulling wagons in the harvest fields. The impetus for mechanisation, especially the harvest, was provided by American, English and Scottish farmers. The early harvesters to arrive in Britain in the 1920's were imported and influenced by the American companies. They were smaller than the American combines but still large and awkward for European conditions, these were tractor drawn with side headers. In America, companies such as Massey-Harris, Minneapolis-Moline, Allis Chalmers, Case, Oliver and John Deere developed new models of trailed and self propelled machines.

Most were trailed reaper threshers, which had worked there since the 1880's on the prairies. Self propelled had not yet been fully accepted. As a result of the two world wars, man power was in short supply, and harvesting methods using binders and threshing machines were labour intensive, there was becoming a need to introduce mechanisation to the harvest fields. In Britain, the combine harvester was not used in any volume until after the Second World War. With wheat production up by 100 percent, mechanisation had arrived to stay, but there were few if any combines being made in the UK.

For centuries, farming had been undertaken with the use of wooden ploughs, harrows, hay rakes and scythes, often home made. Implements were still very primitive. As early as 1826, the Reverend Patrick Bell in Scotland built a primitive harvester. He was one of the first to use rotating knives and a rotating reel. It gained little acceptance in the UK or the US, but it did use some of the features now seen in the modern combine harvester, a front cutting unit, a reel, a front ground land wheel and automatic reaper and was pushed by horses. An American, Samuel Maine was given patents for a travelling thresher in 1828. Another American Obed Hussey in 1834 succeeded in selling a reaper, which was designed for grass with a chassis and two front wheels under the cutting unit and two larger wheels to drive the cutting mechanism. It cut close to the ground, McCormick in 1839 made a reaper harvesting machine which cut higher off the ground. The combine harvester came to Canada with the Moore-Hascall combine which sold in limited numbers in 1836.

Two of the early combine pioneers in California were Daniel Best and Benjamin Holt, whose companies later merged to form Caterpillar. Best whose works were in San Leandro sold combines in 1884. Some firms such as Holt experimented with combine production, but were not successful and no more machines were made. Holt Brothers of Stockton produced their first horse drawn harvester in 1886, followed by further models using steam power. Under Benjamin Holt, later machines appeared, in 1891, Holt made the first "hill-side" combine, capable of keeping the body of the machine level, and so the shaker shoe was level, on steep slopes. These were combines with 50ft cutting widths and some powered by auxiliary gasoline engines. In an effort to cut down on the cost, Holt brought out a smaller combine with 12ft cut. His first self-propelled combines appeared around 1913, but they were adapted trailed models with side-headers and an auxiliary engine to drive the wheels. In 1916, the first front-cut self propelled machine was made, which was mounted on tracks and powered by Ford or Waukesha engines, but these were never made to any extent and were probably not a success. Holt expanded into crawlers, which was a success, leading to the 'Caterpillar' brand. The Best Company and Holt Company had amalgamated in 1925, to form the Caterpillar Tractor

Company. Following this, they ceased making reaper harvesters and sold the rights to Deere and Co.

An early combine included a 16ft cut trailed model by Clayton and Shuttleworth of Lincoln, the threshing machine company, in 1929. These had come and gone by the 1930s. It was the war that established the combine in the UK. In 1942, an Agricultural Machinery Development Board was established, to advise the Ministry of Agriculture about machinery developments and requirements. People were reluctant to change harvesting methods and many said that combines were unsuitable to the damper climate in Britain. There had been only 50 machines working in 1935.

Another early combine was a Claas combine wrapped around a Lanz Bulldog tractor, which appeared in 1930, which was replaced in 1936 by the trailed MDB, which continued in production until later in World War 11 when the factory was put out of action.

The shortage of labour and the need to produce more food for the war effort together with higher grain prices started to change this. By 1939, numbers increased rapidly, and earlier reservations about their suitability were dispelled. The Ministry estimated more combines were needed, about 2,500 for the 1944 harvest and 3,000 for the following year. Several American companies, Case, International Harvester, John Deere and Oliver were building trailed combines in the mid 1930's.

By 1965, British farmers could choose from 32 different combines from 10 manufacturers ranging from the Aktiv trailed PTO driven bagger priced at £805 to the 14ft cut self propelled Bamford's Landlord for £4,000.

The highest population of combines was probably in the 1970's, when the machines were averaging an output of up to 10 tons an hour with headers of 8 to 14ft. Often several were seen working in convoy in the larger fields. Today combines have increased in size with an output in excess of 80 tonnes an hour and 40 foot header widths - similar in width to the early American combines of more than a century ago with a lone giant combine working very often in the largest fields.

The first successful and widely used self propelled combine in the UK was the imported MH 21 designed by Tom Carroll, followed by the British built 726 and 780. Leon Claeys invented the first combine designed for European conditions, the MZ, closely followed by August Claas with the Hercules or renamed SF. Soon many more manufactures joined in. Ransomes were British made, others were imported from the USA, Canada and Europe. Allis Chalmers launched the All Crop 60 in America in 1935, which was made in Britain in the 1950's.

By the early 1950's, the number of combines increased but the majority were towed by a tractor and driven by a separate engine or power take off shaft. Early reaper threshers were horse drawn, later they became tractor powered. In 1938, Massey-Harris introduced the No 20 self propelled combine, followed by the MH No 21 three years later. The first MH 21's came to Britain in 1942, more than 1500 of these combines were in use in Britain at this time. During the war years, but for twenty years after the end of the production of the Clayton combine, most combines in Britain were imported from Canada and the United States. During the Second World War, Massey-Harris No 20, 21 and 22 combines had been in use in Britain, but the Ministry did not want to rely solely on Massey-Harris machines. This led to other manufacturer's machines entering Britain. After the war, the British government imposed tariffs on products from America to reduce imports, making combines expensive. Massey-Harris then began to build combines in Britain to get round the tariff barrier, to increase their sales of combines. The 722 at Manchester was the first of these British built combines.

The number of combines in use on farms in Britain by 1942 was 950, by 1944, the number had risen to 2500, mostly MH 21s and Allis Chalmers All Crops. When the 780 was launched and Manns of Saxham imported the Claas SF Self Propelled machines got bigger. Higher throughput was achieved with an extra beater or various separation systems located just as the crop leaves the concave. These systems help to distribute the crop over the straw walkers, and so greater output was achieved. By the late 1970's operator comfort and safety started to become an issue, leading to advent of cabs, and International Harvester developed the Axial Flow, at the time, the most powerful machine on the market, followed soon after by New Holland. The greatest stride in combine development came in the field of electronics, yield mapping and recording systems, Using GPS Systems, computers lock on to space satellites, and can record the position of the machine down to a few centimetres. Grain flow monitors, moisture meters measure the throughput, all the information being stored in a computer for later evaluation. And so this is how the combine harvester has developed since its first appearance in the harvest fields.

Although many of the trailed combines had been imported into the UK, makes such as Case, Massey-Harris, Oliver, Allis-Chalmers, International Harvester and John Deere, were not British built and were insufficient to meet the growing needs to produce more food.

Many companies soon introduced British built trailed combines, Allis-Chalmers, Marshall, Ransomes and Harrison McGregor and Guest.

Clayton and Shuttleworth of Lincoln had produced the first British built combine harvester in 1928. They made about 30 combines similar to the design of the MH No 5, with its own engine fitted to power the threshing mechanism and a rasp bar type of drum, but the company went bankrupt within two years. When the new owners, Marshalls of Gainsborough bought it in 1930, the Clayton combine was dropped. There were very few combines in Britain, nearly twenty years passed before another British built combine arrived. During that time, UK farmers relied upon imports from Canada and Untied States.

MARSHALLS OF GAINSBROUGH

Marshalls produced their first portable threshing machine in 1849. This was a self propelled combine, the E9 appeared on the market in 1945, which was powered by two 30hp Coventry Climax power units, one for the threshing drum and the other for the transmission and was based on earlier development work on the E7 prototype. The E7 had a 7ft cut, and underwent field trials in around 1943. This model had two 26hp Ford engines, one for the threshing mechanism, and the other to power the transmission and an 8ft cut. These were available as baggers or tanker models. Potential customers were able to see the E9 working at Saundby in Lincolnshire during harvest of 1945. Painted bright silver with green wheels, it was called the 'Silver Queen', but the combine was not a success

and it is thought not many more than fifty units were sold, it was too heavy and had problems with the dressing shoe mechanism, and steering and traction drive. Production ceased in 1947. Marshall then concentrated on developing a trailed combine, influenced by John Deere and Minneapolis-Moline models from the USA. A prototype trailed machine was shown at the Royal Show in 1947 at Lincoln, the first model was the 568 with a 5ft 6in cutting width, followed by two more versions in 1948, the 560 and the largest the 602 having a 5ft 10in cut. They had the same livery as the 'Silver Queen' and had options of crop lifters, and reel attachments. About 1500 were sold, but these combines were not a success, due to Marshall not using the conventional threshing and separating systems. They had used instead one large shaker rack as used in many American combines, which was not suited to the heavier crops and damper climate in the UK. No more were made after 1952.

The Grain Marshall Model 568 was available in 1949 for £750, but was not very successful. In 1952, another improved Marshall combine the 626 appeared. Trials of the Marshall 626 were carried out by the National Institute of Agricultural Engineering in 1954. The NIAE reported that the well built combine gave a good performance in a variety of crops in British harvesting conditions. The new Grain Marshall 626 had a 6ft cut and was available in a bagger or tanker version and went into production at their Gainsborough works. It had an 18in diameter drum, 4 cylinder petrol 20hp Ford engine to power the threshing mechanism and came in orange livery. A trailed machine with reaper gatherer attachment, it required two men to operate it, one on the tractor and the other on the bagging platform. Now straw walkers replaced the single shaker rack, it was lighter and was more efficient than the predecessor. It had been tested in England and Scotland ready for the 1952 harvest when it was available in limited quantities.

Two prototypes of a self propelled combine were built in 1954 and tested on farms in Lincolnshire the following harvests. They performed well, but costs of production and having two engines made it uneconomical to produce and high in maintenance costs. Also due to lack of facilities at the Marshal plant, they were never put to production. Marshalls continued with the trailed 626 until 1958 when the company decided to concentrate on tractor production and no more combines were made.

Demand for trailed combines was falling by the later 1950s and Marshall faced competition for smaller combines from Massey-Harris who had launched the 735.

Albion was another small combine produced in Britain by Harrison, McGregor and Guest and was introduced in 1953 at the Smithfield Show. This had a 4ft cutter bar, and was a pto model with an optional engine drive. An improved 5ft cut power driven model appeared, when the company merged with David Brown, based on a Swedish model, the AB Arvika -Verken, for the 1956 harvest. This was still made in the 1960's as a tanker or bagger model.

McCormick and Deering responded with a 2 man machine in 1917.

BEAVERCROFT

The Beavercroft combine was marketed during the late 1940's by Thornycroft, who were lorry and shipbuilding manufacturers, however only a few were produced due to the combine being beset with design problems. This business originated in 1864 when James Thornycroft built steam launches and developed into a major marine shipbuilding organisation, followed by a steam van in 1895. The combine project began after the war when the need for a British built combine was given priority by the Ministry of Agriculture's Agricultural Machinery Development Board.

Based in Basingstoke, Thorneycroft separated its commercial vehicle haulage business from the shipbuilding business because of Labour Government plans to nationalise the road haulage industry. The combine development began under the original firm, John I Thorneycroft, but details of the machine were released under the new subsidiary company, Transport Equipment (Thorneycroft) Ltd, in 1949. The design was developed by local Hampshire inventor, Eli Beaver of Kempshot, so giving the combine its name. The first prototype painted silver and registered FOT 357 harvested clover seed in Hampshire in 1947 in Hartley Wespall, driven by Norman Beaver, a contractor, assumed to be related to the designer of

the combine. During the 1949 harvest, five further prototypes were on trial, these were all bagger models. It was a straight through machine with 7ft header and four very wide and long walkers, with the sieves being the same width as the drum. The combine utilised many Thorneycroft truck parts, an ER4 four cylinder 65hp petrol engine was used, as in the companies 'Nippy' and 'Sturdy' trucks. The engine and four speed truck gear box were mounted on the chassis longitudinally, and used a truck axle and differential. The layout caused problems, the engine being under the threshing mechanism made maintenance difficult and the design was untidy, including the radiator with the extra pipe work to it because it was mounted on top of the separator housing and the complicated belts and pulleys driving the cooling fan. The driver's platform was above the threshing drum and the gear change mechanism was also complicated, with two levers, one to shift the gate and one for engaging the required gear.

The combine was also top heavy, due to the front and rear axles being narrower than the extra wide threshing system. Small drive wheels had to be fitted to accommodate the wide body and lower the centre of gravity. In wet conditions, the lack of ground clearance resulted in the combine getting bogged in rough ground and open furrows. Some truck components used in the machine could not stand tough harvesting conditions. It appears only six prototypes were produced, one in Lincolnshire only completed a few harvests before going to the scrap yard.

RANSOMES

Ransomes had long experience of threshing machinery manufacture. They were late entering the combine market, they had continued to make threshing machines until the mid 1950's and had been winning medals for their threshing machines in the 1840's at agricultural shows. Founded by a Quaker, Robert Ransome in 1774, the firm began with an ironmongery shop in Norwich. Robert Ransome made cast iron plough shares at foundries in East Anglia. He moved to Ipswich in 1789 and was later joined by his nephew, William Sims and the business expanded in the mid 1800's with the advent of the steam engine, where at their Orwell works, portable steam engines, ploughs and horse rakes were made. John Jefferies married James Ransome's daughter and the firm eventually became known as Ransome Sims and Jefferies in 1884.

Ransomes made an attempt to launch into the combine market in 1946 by converting a threshing box into a trailed combine, with a pick up cylinder and conveyor added to the front and an engine on top of the drum, but this machine was too heavy and it was abandoned. The use of the combine was in ascendancy. An agricultural machinery census recorded 48,000 trailed and self propelled threshing machines in 1959, whereas three years earlier, there were 40,000 combines. In order to meet the immediate harvest demands of its customers, the company imported Swedish built trailed combines in 1953, the Bolinder-Munktell MST42, which they sold as Ransomes MST 42, for use with a 25hp tractor. These were then made under licence at Ipswich by Ransomes for the 1954 harvest. This was a trailed model with 4ft cutter bars and 42in wide threshing cylinders and came with a bagging platform. In 1959 the MST56 replaced the MST 42, which was available as a tanker or bagger model with a wider 5ft cut but the same drum appeared. It required a tractor of 30hp. The cost for a bagger model was then £685. Ransomes also built a prototype MST56 at Ipswich, using a car engine from a Ford Zephyr, but this was never marketed. Instead they decided to concentrate on self propelled combines, making their own. Ransomes expanded their line following a £1.25 million development of the companies Nacton Works in Ipswich.

Ransomes introduced the first Ipswich built pilot model of the 902 in 1956. Pre production machines were tested during the 1957 harvest. The 902 was launched at the 1958 Royal Show as a straight through 6 tons an hour machine, with tanker or bagger model, with a 10ft or 12ft cutter bar, a Reynolds six bat pick up reel and four straw walkers, powered by a 62hp Ford Thames Trader diesel engine with a three forward and one reverse gearbox. The 801 was introduced in 1963 although similar in design to the 901, it was a new machine rather than a scaled down version of the 901. The main difference was that the engine was mounted on top rather than underslung as on the 901.

By 1961, the trailed MST56 was phased out due to lack of demand and a new self propelled combine appeared. The follow up model, the 801, launched for the 1963 harvest, was also available as a tanker or bagger model was claimed to have an output of 3 tons an hour, and had an 8ft cutter bar, 36in wide drum, four straw walkers and was powered by a Perkins 42hp diesel engine. The new 801's Handi-Matic control system enabled the driver to select drum speed, reel and ground speeds from the drivers' seat. By 1964, the four straw walker 1001 replaced this model, with a 10ft and 12ft cut, prices started at £2,695. It was similar to its predecessor, only larger, with output of 6 tons an hour. It came with a choice 62hp 4 cylinder or optional 90hp 6 cylinder Ford diesel engines, and other improvements including disc brakes.

In 1965 Ransomes introduced a prototype high capacity combine, the Cavalier at the Smithfield Show for the 1966 harvest. It was aimed at big acreage growers, with an output of 9 tons an hour. The 1001 was phased out in 1966. At the time, the new 'Early Action' twin drum and concave was a new feature in combine design and claimed to separate up to 25 percent of the grain from the straw at the first drum, before it reached the main drum and concave. The small diameter threshing drum removed much of the grain and fed an even crop flow to the large diameter main cylinder for final threshing. This primary threshing cylinder idea returned to favour in the 1990's. Other features included a special 'cascade' sieve, which combined with the air from the fan removed much of the rubbish from the grain before it reached the top sieve. It also had independent hydraulic controls and claimed to be the first combine with hydrostatic steering. The combine was offered with a two year warranty and option of a cab and Reynolds draper attachment. The Crusader was launched at the Smithfield Show in 1967. A smaller version of this model, replaced the 801, with a 74hp Perkins diesel engine, twin-drum threshing and 10ft or 12ft cutter bar. The smaller Crusader appeared in 1967, and was offered with a 12ft or 14ft header and 90hp six cylinder Ford diesel engine. The 12ft Crusader cost £3,290 in 1969 and the Cavalier cost £3,930. Both these models were made with optional smaller 8ft 6in and 10ft cutter bars later, to meet customer demand. The Crusader with 10ft cut cost from £2,995 when launched but increased to nearly double within five years. A new model to replace the Cavalier, the larger four straw walker 104hp Super Cavalier followed in 1974, with a Perkins diesel engine, and quick release tables from 10ft to 14ft, again using the Twin drum design, This was the last British built combine to be produced, built at the Nacton Road production line in Ipswich. No further combines were made after 1976 due to Ransomes taking the decision that they could not justify the capital outlay on a new model, and the Department of Trade and Industry refused to assist in producing this last prototype, the Saracen. These were built on the Cavalier/Crusader design with wider twin drums and larger engines. Remaining stock was used in the production of a Ransomes sugar-beet harvester.

The idea of the Twin drum, originally developed by Ransomes in the early 1960's disappeared from the market in Britain with the last of the Ransome Super Cavaliers built at Ipswich in 1976, only to be re invented by other manufacturers in the next decade.

As most machines had come from America with different harvesting conditions to the damp climate of Britain, there was a need to build a machine for European conditions. Claas was the first company to experiment with mechanisation geared to the European climate. At Harsewinkel, in Westphalia, Germany, Dr August Claas made the first of many combine harvesters in 1931. The first Claas machine was powered by a Lanz Bulldog tractor, the machine was wrapped around the tractor and had a 6ft cutter bar with a side conveyor to carry the crop to the threshing box at the rear, but this was not a success and was abandoned. The first mass produced combine harvester made for European conditions came from Class, with the MDB-Mah-Dresch-Binder in 1937

CASE AND INTERNATIONAL HARVESTER
— The Case Story

Today the CASE IH brand is associated with the modern Axial Flow combines, now marketed under the CASE IH banner. These were inherited from the International Harvester part of the company. However, J I Case did build several combines from 1923 to 1972, a few of which appeared in the UK.

The origins of J I Case Threshing machine Company of Racine go back to the grain separators and threshers over a period of 110 years. Jerome Increase Case experimented with threshing machines in 1842 and the company still sold a steel drum in 1953. J I Case played a large part in the mechanisation of grain harvesting in America, concentrating on threshers and other equipment rather than reapers.

The acquisition of the Emerson Brantingham line in 1928 then added binders to the range. The first Case combine appeared in 1923, designed for prairie farms, it combined a Case thresher with a grain header and was designed by Thomas Dugan of Wichita. An engineer Leon R Clausen from John Deere began to develop new designs of combines for Case from 1924. These were known as the 'A' , 'H', 'P' 'A' and 'W' models, launched in the 1920s, they were designed for the Mid West. The model 'P' a Prairie combine was developed from the original Case harvester, with a 12ft or 16ft header with toothed drum and powered by a Case engine from a tractor. A new range of smaller more compact combines were made at the newly acquired Burlington plant Iowa in 1937.

The Case Model Q was one of the first combine harvesters to work in East Anglia in 1936. This was a reaper-thresher with 12ft cutter bar and a gravity emptied grain tank, it had a 32in diameter peg drum powered by a Case petrol-paraffin engine. It was imported by the Associated Manufacturers at the Palace of Industry in Wembley who later exhibited it at the Royal Show. The model 'Q' was based on the model 'P' and had a wheel for operating the table height on the operator's platform it also had a meter to record grain in the tank. One model which has worked on a Suffolk farm until retirement in the Second World War is still preserved by combine collector Ron Knight. By this time, more compact combines appeared from Case. The Case peg drum was replaced by rasp bars on the model 'G'.

Case pull type combines were developed further in the 1950's, with the 55, a 5ft cut power drive machine and Model 110 with 10ft or 12ft cut. The SP 9 and SP 12 were the first Case Self Propelled combines. Launched in 1951, the 9ft cut SP 9 used an engine from the S series tractor range and the 12ft cut SP 12 was powered by a D power unit. All combines were now made at Bettendorf Iowa and these models evolved into the 120 and 150 models.

By the 1960's, the 800 and 1000 models appeared, these were three and four straw walker machines with standard rasp bar drums with the spike tooth being offered as an option. They came as gas, diesel or LPC engines. These were later replaced by the 700 and 1010 with straw walkers and the 600 model which had a single piece shaker rack instead of walkers, this model offered features ahead of its time, such as hydraulic table controls, variable speed and hydrostatic steering. Popular in the Mid West, few entered Britain, but one with a 10ft cut and Case four cylinder diesel engine from their 630 tractor, was registered in 1964 in Nottinghamshire is now in Ron Knights collection near Stamford. Case had in the meantime ventured into the rapidly expanding construction equipment market at Burlington, so by 1972 Case decided to cease combine manufacture.

However, the 1985 merger between the Case Corporation and International Harvester brought IHC Axial Flow combines of recent years under the CASE IH banner. The latest 20 series range with the flagship 9120 model claims to be the biggest combine in North America, having a 523hp engine, and 350 bushel grain tank. This model has now made its debut in Britain.

ORIGINS OF IH – THE MCCORMICK CONNECTION

In July 1831, Cyrus Hall McCormick launched a reaper to mechanically harvest grain. McCormick radically changed harvesting practices in the 19th century. Several other reaper companies were formed in the second half of the 19th century. In August 1902, the International Harvester Company was formed when four other major reaper companies and McCormick harvesting merged into one company which became known as IH. These were McCormick Harvesting Machine Company, Deering Harvester Co, Plano Machinery Company, Champion, Bushnell and Glessner Company and the Milwaukee Harvester Co. Most International products sold in the US became known as McCormick Deering.

IH first experimented with a harvester in 1913. IH was the first of the large manufactures to enter the combine market, with the No 1 in 1914, a pull type, followed by a tractor drawn combine in 1925.

In Britain, the International Harvester No 8 combine underwent field trials after it become the first harvester thresher to be exhibited at the Royal Show in 1928. It was a pto model but had an option of a petrol auxiliary engine, it was a 10ft bagger machine. This had the American peg type drum, rather than the later beater or rasp-bar type drums. The peg type tended to shatter the straw. They were often pulled by Lanz Bulldog tractors, because of their weight and their steel wheels on soft ground.

Self-propelled models followed in 1942, the No 123 SP which had hydraulic platform control, 6 cylinder engine and a 12ft header. These were manufactured in East Moline, Illinois.

INTERNATIONAL HARVESTER IN BRITAIN

The International Harvester Company had become well established in America, making a range of Self-propelled and trailed combines. International had been in the combine business for thirty years with several trailed harvester-reapers working in Britain since the 1930's. The company altered its combine designs in 1940 with the introduction of the 4ft cut No 42 power take-off driven combine, with streamlined and painted tinwork, instead of galvanised steel, and a straight through arrangement instead of the header being off-set. In 1941, the larger 6ft No 62 was first made and was exported to Britain, which has three straw walkers. This had a new appearance, being made from curved steel pressings. It is thought that around 43,000 of these were made over ten years, with many coming to the UK. The War Agricultural Executive Committees had been operating the International trailed No 62 combine built in Chicago America, and received favourable reports. The International Harvester Company of

Great Britain arranged for twenty of these models to be allotted for use under the 'lend-lease' provisions for the harvest in 1944, and to be tested for suitability in the British climate. The No 62 was replaced by the No 64 in 1951.

McCormick opened a factory in Chicago in 1837 where he manufactured reapers on a large scale.

In 1930 McCormick joined the Deering Company, and was one of the founders of the International Harvester Company. The McCormick-Deering 123-SP was launched in 1942, this was the Company's first self propelled combine and it retained some of the features seen in the No 62, the curved separator housing pressings, elevators and threshing mechanism. It was slightly larger with four walkers and larger drum with a 12ft cutter bar, and had a self emptying grain tank, although a bagging platform was available. It had an International Green Diamond engine taken from a truck, which was a six cylinder side valve unit of 45hp. Components such as the walkers and header were sourced from various other combines, the four speed gearbox was taken from a truck and other parts - the steering wheel and seat came from Farmall tractors. The B-64 built in Doncaster which was similar to the American No 64, was introduced in Britain at the 1952 Smithfield Show. This came as a bagger or tanker model, some were PTO-driven, while others had a petrol PAV4 air-cooled auxiliary engine. The B-64 was typical of the straight through design preferred by most combine manufacturers at the time. It has a 6ft cut, threshing cylinder, straw walkers and grain sieves and averaged 3 tons of wheat an hour according to field tests. The F8.63 McCormick International self propelled combine was a tanker /bagger model with a 7ft header and could be switched over from tanking to bagging in a few minutes.

International Harvester evolved from a group of small manufacturers of reapers and binders in the US. By 1902 the preliminary terms of the merger were settled, the McCormick, Deering, Plano, Milwaukee and Champion lines combined to form the IHC. Control of the new company would rest in the hands of a three member voting trust - Cyrus McCormick, Charles Deering and George Perkins. The five largest producers of harvesting equipment were consolidated and IHC had under its control 90% of the nation's trade in grain binders. Cyrus Hall McCormick and Charles Deering were the principal agents in the formation of IHC, they were sons of the harvesting pioneers and together successfully launched the new corporate company known as IHC International Harvester Company. Their factory was based in Chicago.

THE ARRIVAL OF THE ROTARY COMBINE

The conventional combine with a cylinder and concave threshing and straw walkers and round hole or adjustable sieves for the separation were still in vogue, but combines by the 1980's were getting bigger with outputs in excess of 18 tons an hour and engines were now over 200hp.

The Axial Flow was introduced in America by International Harvester in 1977, using a principle that can be traced back 100 years. In 1979, a few were sent to the UK, France and Germany. By 1981 all IH combines were turned over to rotary models. A new factory was built in France and production started in 1983, to meet the demand for Axial Flow combines.

Other manufactures experimented with rotary combines, MF and John Deere developed their versions. The NH combine had longitudinal rotors but was not a success in the UK and it was only sold in the drier Southern European countries. The NH TF42 was a more successful model. Massey-Ferguson developed the massive 8590, but this too did not survive. Claas added a new separating system with 8 rotary separators and concaves in 1981 to their Dominator 116, the CS model. At this time, the bulk of rotary development took place with the Axial Flow made by International Harvester.

The East Moline plant produced the Axial Flow later in 1977, which was made to adapt to many different crops.

The 1400 series consisted of three models ranging from a 13ft cut 1420 with a 124hp engine to the 210hp 1480 with a 22ft 6in cut.

The 1440 and 1460 were introduced in 1977 with an initial run of 300 machines, followed by the larger 1480 in 1978, which had a DT 436 engine, 30in rotor and 208 bushel grain tank.

The 1440 had a DT 436 IH engine, 24in rotor and 145 bushel grain tank. The 1460 had a 170hp DT 436 IH engine, 24in rotor and 180 bushel grain tank.

Changes to the Axial Flow models in 1979 included new engine design for the 1440 and 1460, - the turbocharged engines became 'B' series engines. All models were hydrostatic drive only coupled to 3 speed transmission, hydraulically activated discharge auger, and a shaft speed monitor was available. The 1480 had a fuel tank capacity of 123 gal and 1440/1460 had capacity of 92 galls.

All models used three piece concaves of which there were two sizes, the small were for wheat and small grains and the large wire concaves were for corn and other crops grown in the US. In the back half of the rotor cage, there were three separating grates, available in a slotted style for most crops or bar style for conditions requiring more aggressive separation. The 1480 had four impeller blades and a rotor, the 40 to 60 models had three blades. Adjustable vanes on the rotor cage controlled the speed of the crop through the rotor cage area. A four blade discharge beater expelled the crop material coming off the back of the rotor to a pair of spreaders which spread the material on the ground. The fan was a 6 blade paddle type.

In 1980, the 1420 Axial Flow was introduced - this had a header of up to 20ft and 112hp diesel engine which was made in IH's factory in Neuss, Germany. This was the first IH combine using electro hydraulic controls which utilized electrical switches to activate solenoid controlled hydraulic valves, so replacing levers, knobs, cables and mechanical linkages used previously.

Later a hillside model the 1470 was introduced with a 210hp DT 466 engine and 145 bushel tank. This offered hydrostatic transmission. International by now sold only rotary combines and electro hydraulic controls were incorporated into all IH combines in 1981.

The model 8-15 one of the last of the walker machines made with a 10-24 ft header was built until 1976 with a 128hp diesel engine and 133 bushel grain tank. Now Case IH only sells walker machines in Europe.

The Axial Flow system featured a single line rotor with impeller on the front rotor and a stationery rotor housing with concaves and separating grates. In 1977, IH introduced the 1440, 1460 and 1480 which took 15 years to design.

In 1977 and 1978, Axial Flows continued to use the 810 grain header series used on the 15 series of walker machines.

In 1979, the 820 series of headers were introduced.

FORMATION OF CASE IH

In November 1984, IH sold the agricultural equipment business to Tenneco, the parent company of J.I Case. IH had been having financial difficulties in 1980/1981, the agricultural economy at this time was uncertain, this led to the sell off to a suitable buyer, and CASE IH was formed. Axial Flows were continued to be manufactured at East Moline. The white cabs of the 1400 series were changed to red and the decals now read 'Case International'. During the 1984 to 1985 period, Case ceased combine production in Europe as did MF.

The 1600 series CASE IH Axial Flows were introduced in 1985 for the following season and featured a few refinements compared to the 1400's which they replaced, including standard header reverser, extension for the concaves to enable better threshing capacity and improvements to the unloading auger. There were four models using the DT 466 engines.

The 1680 225hp to 1620 124hp model.

1660 100hp was added to that of the previous model

1640 150hp

1620 124hp

The 1620 hillside and pull type combines were discontinued in 1991.

J I Case Europe then based at Wheatley Road Doncaster in South Yorks had the 160hp 1640, 190hp 1660 and 235hp 1680 available in 1989, for prices ranging from £68,191 for the smallest model to £89, 779 for the 1680.

In 1993 CASE IH introduced the 1644/1666/1688 models, which had many changes such as Cross Flow fan replacing the paddle type fan to give more volume of air to the sieves, but these model numbers were not used in Europe. They ranged from the 1644 with 180hp engine, to the 1666 215hp model and the 1688 260hp model. This was the last model of the first generation of Axial Flow combines dating back to 1977.

In 1995, Case became a company independent of Tenneco. The 2100 series appeared, with a new cab design. This model had large heavy duty final drives to support the extra weight of larger headers required for larger capacity combines. New features included - The combination service brake/park brake was new design multi disc units which ran in oil all the time requiring minimal pedal effort to actuate.

The hydraulic system was redesigned from the 1600 series, it now utilized a pressure and flow compensated (PFC) hydraulic pump for its main functions. The pump creates very little flow when there is no demand on the hydraulic system, saving hp and fuel while creating less heat in the hydraulic system. The pump is used for the steering, header lift and lower functions, unloader swing in and out, reel lift and fore and aft functions.

Feeder lift cylinders were larger in diameter requiring only two lift cylinders instead of three on the 1600 series. A gear pump mounted in tandem with the PFC Pressure and Flow Compensated pump, supplied oil for the hydraulic reel drive, brake functions, and un loader on off functions and for engaging the separator.

In 1996 there were many changes to the 2100 series engines, including new injection pumps, injectors pistons and cylinder heads.

As far as engines and horse power went, little changed from the later 1644/66/88 models. The PFC hydraulic system gave these models more HP without having to have bigger engines.

In 1996, the Axial Flow combine became available with the yield monitor and GPS mapping system which Case called Advanced Farming systems. A sensor in the elevator measured grain flowing past it, and a sensor in the grain delivery auger or grain tank auger measured grain moisture and temperature. Monitors in the cab gave constant readings. Used with the GPS system, the farmer could pin point areas in a field for best and poorest yields.

Many new Axial Flow features were launched on the 2300 series replacing the 2100 series.

Case celebrated the Silver Anniversary in 2002.

When the 2388 was launched, it was an entirely different machine to what the market already had - a full rotary with one single longitudinally mounted.

CT walker machines launched in 2002, at the CNH factory in Zedelgem Belgium discontinued the 5050-5080 series.

Case combines are made in the US with the UK office headquarters being based at Basildon.

The AFX 8010 was launched in 2004, which sold alongside the smaller 2300 series. Improvements include the AFX rotor, less belts and chains, more hydraulics, inverted rotary screen which gives the engine a natural air flow, electronic controlled sieves and screens, programmable, new cab, longer feeder house, bigger elevators, augers well as updated cosmetics. The All hydraulic rotor drive is hydraulic with reverser. The 8010 is 400hp, and is hooked up electronically with the rotor drive, so in harder crops, the engine will up the hp and in easier crops, the hp will drop off to conserve fuel. The AFX is produced along with NH's CR combine with Twin-Rotor technology in Grand Island Nebraska. The AFX combines share common parts with the NH CR combine including durable CNH frame and large grain tank from 205 to 330 bushels with foldable extensions

The AFX Series combine still shares some similar design features as the original Axial-Flow introduced in 1977. The new AFX rotor uses enhanced graduated pitch impellers to promote smooth crop flow and increase rotor throughput capacity in tough conditions by 5 to 25 percent. The top of the range AFX 8010 is a Class 8 combine with around 370hp and capable of handling up to a 42ft header.

9010 IN 2007

The 10 series changed to 20 series for 2009.
2388's replaced by the new 88 series in 2009.
2009 models: 5088, 6088 7088 launched late 2008 for 2009 season.
7120, 8120 and 9120 launched for 2009 season.

CLAEYS, CLAYSON, NEW HOLLAND, CNH

COMPANY NAMES
Dates when registered following mergers

1906-Werkhuizen Leon Claeys private company
1939-PVBA Werkhuizen Leon Clayes
1964-Werkhuizen Leon Claeys
1967-Clayson N.V.
1977-Sperry Rand Belgium N.V.
1979-Sperry N.V.
1985-Sperry New Holland International N.V.
1986-New Holland N.V.
1987-Ford New Holland N.V.
1992-New Holland Belgium N.V.
2002-CNH Belgium N.V.

HISTORY OF CLAEYS

Leon's Father, Louis Claeys was a blacksmith who also had a small farm, where Leon learnt the skills of the trade. Leon later repaired and assembled bicycles in his Father's blacksmith shop. By 1903 Leon's bicycle business was prospering. Leon went to Hennef in Germany, where he learnt new techniques and methods at a foundry owned by Jacobi, which made agricultural tools. On his return, Leon began to import treadmills and threshing machines from this firm, and installed them on local farms.

Leon then started his own business, renting some ground from a brewer in Veldegem behind the inn. He built his first threshing machines in 1906, this marked the beginnings of the Zedelgem factory. Claeys also built petrol engines and later diesel engines, he was a friend of Robert Diesel, the inventor of the diesel engine. The first diesels were heavy and were mostly used to drive stationery threshing machines. Claeys branched into tractor production in 1947 followed by the first tractor pulled combine and later self propelled combines. Tractor production ceased but the combine production went from strength to strength.

Being the first self propelled combine harvester in Europe, the development is worth a mention. In 1947 the stationery thresher was at the height of its success. Straw shaking parts for grain and chaff separation and wind controlled sieves for cleaning were added to the threshing machines, and some were engine powered. Later models which Claeys made were by now beginning to look like the future combine harvester. From American imports, it was clear that the next step was to combine cutting and threshing. The pull type combine came next. The first Claeys self propelled combine, the MZ was exhibited at the Paris Agricultural show in 1952, and was the first European self propelled combine. Another model, the MD was also built, the only difference from the MZ being the drum and cutting width. Due to shortage of funds, the first MZ was built using truck gearboxes and steering wheels, bought from "Stock American" shops specializing in the use of used military equipment components, the engines were rebuilt. This was the beginning of a massive expansion and the foundations of New Holland Zedelgem's position today. The second Series MZ combines in 1953 used Perkins and Austin engines.

New Holland had belonged to the US holding company, Sperry Rand Corporation since 1947. Associations with New Holland began when the French Claeys importer, Sotradies was importing balers from the American company. Claeys exhibited a New Holland baler at the Brussels Agricultural Fair in 1957. In May 1964, the Sperry Rand Corporation, a U.S. holding company to which New Holland had belonged since 1947 now bought 51% of the Claeys company shares.

In 1963, the company name was also changed from Claeys to Clayson. Yet another change of name followed in 1977 when the company became known as Sperry Rand Belgium N.V.

Later, there were further changes when Sperry New Holland the agricultural machinery division of the US Company was sold to Ford Motor Company in 1986 and the largest division of Sperry Rand division, Sperry Univac was merged to form a global information technology company called Unisys. Claeys had been a large Ford engine customer in the 1960's. The Company was now known as New Holland N.V before becoming Ford New Holland N.V. in 1987.

The New Holland company emerged from this merger which brought together two giants of the business. By now New Holland had become a global leader in the construction equipment industry.

Another change came in the 1990 when the Fiat Group announced the planned acquisition of Ford New Holland and its merger with Fiat Geotech, the farm construction machinery division of Fiat. Out of this merger came Ford New Holland NV and this was registered in 1992. New Holland was listed in the New York Stock Exchange in 1996, with Fiat being the majority shareholder.

In the 1990's, some combines were made by New Holland under license in Poland, and marketed by Fiat Agri, in their livery, including the L series with Integrale self levelling system, and L MCS models, with Multi Crop Separator. These models were only marketed for a short time.

THE LAST MERGER - THE COMPANY TODAY

CNH was formed through the merger of the Case Corporation and New Holland N.V. in 1999. CNH is one of the worldwide leaders in agricultural and construction machinery and has one of the largest equipment finance companies, together with being a world wide leader in agricultural machinery. They produce one of the most extensive range of tractors for all working situations, and specialist equipment such as the rotary combines, grape harvesters and cotton pickers.

Today, CNH markets its products under the brand names of New Holland, Steyr and Case IH, with the Zedelgem plant manufacturing New Holland combines, balers and forage harvesters and some Case IH products.

Following New Holland's purchase of a controlling interest in Leon Claeys in 1964, Bamford's who had held the franchise since 1958, announced that it was relinquishing the marketing of Clayson combines in the UK. The combines would now be distributed by the New Holland Machinery Company of Aylesbury.

Bamford's dealer, Platts Ltd started selling the yellow combines in UK. The Platts Harris Agricultural Group Ltd based at Newark have sold over 2,000 combines produced at Zedelgem.

JOHN DEERE

This company eventually became the largest combine manufacturer in North America, but was a late entrant to the combine market.

The common European combine design of having the grain tank behind the driver and the engine behind the grain tank was first used by John Deere on the 55 model. Allis Chalmers Gleaner also adopted this layout on the Gleaner in the early 1950's.

History of John Deere

The young John Deere learnt blacksmithing in his native Vermont, producing hay forks, horseshoes and hoes. In 1936, he moved to Grand Detour in Illinois to further his skills and following demands for a plough which would cut cleanly through the Mid West thick earth, he invented a polished steel plough by curving a broken steel saw mill blade. This helped the pioneer farmers to open the American prairies to agriculture. In the US, the plough business grew and by 1848, John Deere moved to Moline, where he later made wooden wagons and grain drills. In 1859, when Deere's son Charles inherited direction of the company, other implements were to follow, including a horse drawn grain binder in 1911. A tractor drawn binder which he launched in 1929, the fore runner of the combine harvester, with a 10ft cut harvested twice as much corn as the 8ft binder. During the years of the First World War, there were mechanical advances, farms grew larger as the workforce declined. In 1940, the 12A combine was launched in the US, this was a pull type with a 6ft cut, and was the beginnings of John Deere's combine manufacture. The 12 A was a popular combine, and was imported into Britain by Jack Olding, it was driven by a tractor pto, or supplied with a EA-92 auxilliary engine. It was in production from 1940 to 1952. By 1955, a self propelled combine followed, which featured an auger platform with retracting fingers in the middle.

John Deere began developing harvester threshers in the 1920's and expanded its line further in 1936 after acquiring the rights to the Holt-Caterpillar combines.

The company began making combines in the US in 1927, the first self propelled machine, a 55 model was available in 1946 as a production machine. It is known that only two 55 models were exported to UK in 1948, the model became the leader in its field with no teething problems. Don Macmillan imported a larger 95 model for use on his own farm in 1959. A 55c had the engine behind the grain tank adopting its final position, but the operator was still off set, but this model was a step closer to the final design production unit where the driver was centralized, offering a layout copied by many competitors. In 1946, the John Deere 55 was very advanced and according to JD sources, it was more copied than any other combine before or since. The first Claeys MZ, eventually the M113, was virtually the same machine widened in the separator from 30in to 40in for the heavy straw grown in Europe, and the Massey-Harris 20 and 21 are said to be modelled on the JD 55. The American parent company, Deere and Co purchased the Heinrich Lanz factory in Mannheim West Germany in 1956, which is still the main European manufacturing base today.

John Deere combines have been imported into the UK since 1958. The 530 and 630 combines were in the company's product line up at the beginning of 1966, when John Deere Limited first started trading in the UK and Ireland from Langar. Prior to this, JD combines could be bought from various importers from the late 1930's onwards, initially from Standens Huntingdonshire. H Leverton of Spalding also imported John Deere machines from 1937 to 1950 and Don Macmillan of Devizes imported used tractors and machinery from 1950 to 1958. Between 1958 to 1960, Fred Myers was appointed the first UK dealer, he imported Deere Agricultural and industrial machines from Mannheim.

In 1964, John Deere Ltd purchased an ex Canadian Forces Medical Store at Langar.

All the German built John Deere combines have been based on the classic American 55 combine design. The 72hp 55 was a three straw walker combine, with headers from 12 to 14ft and drum dimensions of 22in x 30in with 62/65 bushel grain tank. John Deere made a major contribution to combine design with the 55 in 1946, which was the first machine in the industry to centre the operator on top and locate the engine and grain tank directly behind the operator, giving better weight balance and a cleaner quieter location for the engine. In 1964, the first combine came off the production line at Zweibrucken, one the legendary 30 series, the 330 followed by the 430 and 530. These were made at Manheim before the decision was made to move self propelled combine production to Zweibrucken in 1964.

In 1965, John Deere introduced the 630 combines, which were the first to be made in Zweibrucken in Germany. These machines were designed to harvest the high yields and long straw of the grain crops in Europe and were fitted with a 100hp Perkins engine, 41in cylinder, 4 straw walkers and 90 bushel tank with header options of 10ft to 14ft.

In 1967, the pull type 360 was launched with either a 7ft or 7ft 9in cutting platform, replacing the 330, it could be fitted with its own hydraulic system or used with the tractors hydraulic system. Reel lift, table heightand threshing mechanism engagement was controlled from the tractor seat. The machine had a drum diameter of 24in and three straw walkers and it was aimed at the smaller capacity market.

In 1975, the 955 combine was introduced with a John Deere engine of 117hp. This model had a 41in wide cylinder and 4 walkers, 80 bushel tank and header options of 10ft to 16ft.

By the 1970's combines with hydrostatic transmission appeared. In the US John Deere launched the 7720 in 1977, with this feature and larger grain tanks and engines. By 1989, the 9600 appeared with more emphasis on greater operator comfort, the 9000 series were designed for worldwide use.

The 1175 which was built in Horizontina Brazil, was similar to an earlier model made at Zweibrucken, which had a 51in wide cylinder, five walkers and a 137 bushel grain tank. In 1989, John Deere of Langar was marketing the 105hp 1055 priced at £34,593, together with the 1100 series, the 125hp 1166, 1174 and 1169H to the 150 hp 1177 and 200hp 1188H4 hillside model, which had a list price of £76,971

The 9750 STS launched in 1999 uses tines on a single rotor in a cage to expand the crop as it progresses to the rear, giving a high crop flow and capacity and good separation. This at the time was the largest JD combine with a 325hp engine and 300 bushel grain tank capacity.

Today, the S690i is made at the Harvester Works at East Moline Illinois

USA, the C Series and T series are made at Zweibrucken and the 1470 and 1570 mid spec machines are made at Horizontina Brazil.

MASSEY FERGUSON

Origins of Massey Ferguson

Massey Ferguson was formed by a merger between Massey Harris and the Ferguson tractor company in 1953, creating the company Massey Harris Ferguson. Massey Harris of Toronto in Canada had a large influence on combine development. The company had a long harvest history in Europe and Australia with their stripper harvester introduced in 1901.

The firm was founded in 1847 in Newcastle Ontario, by Daniel Massey as the Newcastle Foundry and Machine Manufactory, making some of the world's first mechanical threshers. At first they assembled parts from the US and later designed and built their own equipment. Daniel's eldest son, Hart Massey took over and expanded the firm, which was renamed Massey Manufacturing Co, and moved to Toronto Canada. In 1891, H A Massey of Toronto who had pioneered harvest implements in the mid 19th century merged with the A Harris, Son and Co Ltd of Brantford Ontario, to become Massey-Harris and at that time became the largest agricultural equipment supplier in the British Empire, making threshing machines and reapers. By 1890, both were making the same products.

In 1910, the company acquired the Johnson Harvester Company located in Batavia New York. Today the company exists as Massey Ferguson, a brand name used by AGCO.

Massey had connections with McKay when in 1955 Massey purchased the Australian H V McKay company, manufacturers of the brand name Sunshine.

Hugh Victor McKay had invented the stripper harvester in 1884, the first machine to combine the functions of reaping, threshing and winnowing grain from the standing crop. McKay later established a manufacturing base at Ballarat and then transferred to Braybook Junction re-named Sunshine in 1907 after the harvester's brand name. McKay manufactured stripper harvesters in the 1890's and at the turn of the century. By the 1920's, the McKay company was running the largest implement factory in the southern hemisphere and were leading the international agricultural industry through the development of the words first self-propelled harvester in 1924. In 1930, H. V. McKay Company was granted exclusive Australian distribution of Massey Harris machinery. The company was then renamed H.V. McKay Massey Harris Pty Ltd and throughout World War II they exported over 20,000 Sunshine drills, harrows and binders to England to aid increased food production.

THE FIRST TRAILED MH COMBINES THE CLIPPER 750

Massey Harris officially entered the combine market in 1910 with the No 1 Reaper Thresher aimed at the Australian market. This was a ground driven horse drawn machine. This was the forerunner of the No 5 machine. In 1922, an engine was fitted to power the threshing mechanism. Massey Harris was one of the first to use rasp bar threshing drums instead of peg drums, to produce a better grain sample. A few No 5's were being evaluated in the UK. Reaper threshers were trailed pull type machines, and became tractor PTO driven in the 1920's.

Massey Harris were the pacemakers in combine design. During the 1930's, they offered the No 15 and in 1937 the "Clipper", both fairly low cost and driven off the tractor pto. Production started on the trailed bagger combine, the 750 in 1953, but this did not sell well. A British version of the No 50, it had a 5ft cut with a Standard vaporising engine or a Wisconsin petrol unit, in Canada. They were sold at the same time as the Number 21 and 22 combines. The trailed 'Clipper' combine, a tanker or bagger model, was introduced with 4ft 6in, 6in and 7ft cutting widths. It was later self propelled and made in the USA at the Batavia plant in New York. MH launched the No 750 in the UK based on this machine.

MH NUMBER 20, 21 AND 22

The inventor of the self propelled combine was an Australian, Tom Caroll, who was the chief engineer of the harvesting equipment division at Massey Harris, the first model came off the production line in 1938. The MH 20 and 722 were the first combines to really invade the British market in the post war years and they set the scene for the later 726 and 780 self propelled machines made in the UK.

The Canadian built MH No 20 combine with a 16ft cut was released in 1938, and was developed in Argentina, this evolved from the test prototype No 19, and was the first MH Reaper thresher to become known as a combine harvester. It was powered by a 65hp 6 cylinder Chrysler engine.

In 1940 the No 21 appeared in the UK, imported from Canada. The 21 revolutionised farming both here and in the US, and 1500 were shipped to the UK during the war on the Lease-Lend scheme. With wartime food shortages, there was a need for mechanisation. The 21 had a canvas table, while the 21A had an auger table, with electric lift and the Chrysler engine placed underneath the combine in the centre, between the drum and straw walkers. It had a 12ft cut. This was joined by the No 22 with 8ft cut in 1944. Aimed at the smaller farmer, it was powered by a 35hp four cylinder Continental petrol engine and had a variable speed vee-belt drive, and came as a bagger or tanker model. After the war MH harvesters were made beyond Canada, in the UK, France and Germany. The No 22 joined the No 20 and No 21 and trailed 'Clipper' combines already in Britain.

THE FIRST MH COMBINE THE 722

The first UK MH combine, the No 722 was based on these models and it was the only MH combine made at the company's Barton Dock Road factory in Manchester. MH Production of the 722 was phased out when it was transferred to the new MH factory in Kilmarnock where the MH 726 and MH 780 followed.

THE 726

Introduced in 1948, the 726 had an 8 ft 6in cutter bar, 2ft wide drum, 4 straw walkers and the option of a bagging off platform or grain tank. The 726 went into production at the new Kilmarnock factory in 1949. It had a Petrol/tvo six cylinder Austin Newage ohv engine or a petrol Morris four cylinder unit of 59hp, and it had an electric table lift. This machine was the same as the No 26 in Canada, which had a 8ft 6in, or 12ft cut and was available in a tanker or bagger version. From 1948, the 726 and 722 were the first combines to be fitted with on the move variable speed transmission, which was undertaken via a belt operating on variable pulleys.

THE 726 AND 780

In the 1950's, MH red combines dominated the harvest fields, the 726 and 780 were very popular models in the UK, and in 1955, MHF supplied 90% of combines sold in Britain.

THE MH 780

Various other models were launched from Canada for the North American market. During this era, combine production began in France at Marquette and Eschwege in Germany, at first to supply the French combine market. The Company strategy was to build small combines in Eschwege, medium combines in Kilmarnock and large combines in France.

In the UK the 780 was launched for the 1954 harvest, based on the Canadian No 80. It had an 8ft or 10ft header with a petrol 56hp Austin Newage six cylinder petrol/tvo or 61hp Perkins L4 diesel engine. The drum size of the 780 increased to 32in. The 12ft cut MH 780 was introduced in 1955 with electric table lift and mechanical gearbox. The 24 forward speeds used in the 726 was retained, and it came with the choice of a 6 cylinder Austin or 4 cylinder Morris petrol engine.

The Massey Harris 780 was succeeded by the MF version in 1959.

When Massey-Harris merged with Ferguson, the 780 was altered with increased cleaning area and longer straw walkers, and the electric table was replaced by a single acting hydraulic ram, together with other improvements. The 1956 range of 780 combines which finally replaced the 726, included 8ft 6in and 10ft cutter bars and choice of Newage Austin petrol or TVO engine or Perkins L4 Diesel. A 1956 MH 780 with 12ft cut and diesel engine cost £1,745. There were by now hydraulically operated variator pulleys for traction belt and hydraulic table lift rams, but sprockets still had to be changed to alter drum and reel speeds.

THE 735

The 735 was introduced in 1956 and was designed for smaller acreages with an overall width of 7ft 7in. It had a 6ft header, 4 cylinder 24hp Austin TVO or BMC Newage petrol engine with magneto ignition and came as either a bagger or tanker model. The table lift was hand operated. Farm safety regulations now began to appear, the user was advised to keep the spare sieves in their brackets to serve as safety guards for the belt and chain drives.

The 780 Special, the successor to the 780, had a more advanced table lift, which now became hydraulic instead of the electric lift and also speed control could be undertaken hydraulically with reel adjustment from the driver's seat. The 780 Special was UK built. This was a streamlined version of the 780, similar in style to the Canadian 82 and 92. After the last stocks of 780's were finished in 1962, the 788 appeared from Kilmarnock in 1962, for the 1963 season, which was really a restyled 780, and was more or less the same only with a new body. It had a new style straw walker hood, the reverse slope of the straw walker hood was a noticeable feature, as well as the horizontal cooling air intake for the radiator, a hinged grain unloading auger, and safety guards.

THE 400 AND 500

The 400 and 500 models came in the 1960's, and were made at Kilmarnock. These new machines set the style of combines for the next 20 years and were designed to compete with the increasing number of foreign machines on the British market. These were introduced in 1962, initially with 8ft 6in and 10ft headers, but by 1963, a 12ft cut was added

to the 500 for the price of £2,750. They were ahead of their time in design and engineering, with many new features, including a rotary air screen to throw out the dust, disc brakes and the saddle grain tanks mounted on either side of the body. A rethresher was another feature. The tanker model 400 had a 72hp Perkins A4.300 engine, and came in widths of 8ft to 12ft. The larger 500 with headers of 10 to 14 ft and 94hp Perkins engine was aimed at the contractor or larger farmer. Outputs of over 7 tons an hour were claimed. The 500 at the time was one of the most advanced machines on the market, with automatic table height control with ground sensing fingers introduced in 1963. Production at Kilmarnock continued and by 1971, MF had eight different models with hydrostatic steering, hydraulic disc brakes and a 16ft table was added. Most were 'Quick-Attach' tables and engine power had now increased to over 100hp.

The MF 400 with 72hp and 500 with 94hp engines were upgraded gradually through different models to end with the MF525 and 625 Super 11 respectively. The yellow swirl on the rotary screen which rotated at high speed to throw off dirt and chaff from the air stream to the radiator was a feature of the 400's and 500's.

THE 410, 415, 510 AND 515

Other models followed from the 400 and 500, with the 410, 415, 510 and 515 being introduced from 1965 to 1966. The 510, 515, 520, 525, 535, 620, 625 models, Super 11 models were made in the UK.

The 510 and 515 looked the same as the 500 but were wider, with larger separating areas, and the MF "Multi Flow", seen on the 415 and 515 appeared. On the rear of the combine, this feature allowed the straw coming off the walkers to pass down a steep pan with metal combs in the bottom. A rotary beater knocked the straw against the pans as it passed through the comb onto the grain pan. Engine sizes increased to 80hp and 104hp for the 510/515. A new design of header, the MF 'Quick Attach' Table also appeared on these models, enabling it to be removed by one person, quickly and towed behind the combine on a trolley. Automatic table height was now standard with hydraulic reel control from the drivers' seat, and a wobble box knife drive now replaced the old pitman knife-drive.

The 525 and 625 end of Kilmarnock

In the 1970's the 525 and 625 series replaced the 410, 510 and 515 models. According to a Massey Ferguson source, the announcement was made in 1979 about the Kilmarnock closure and it finally closed in 1980. A spin-off Company (Moorfield Manufacturing) continued to make some machinery and components for Massey Ferguson for a few years on the same site. The MF 520 / 525 Super II and MF 620 / 625 Super 11 were the last to be built in Britain, (a source states that the MF 620 Super 11 was made in Britain from 1979 to 1982, some models would still show in inventories after the closure of Kilmarnock).

When Kilmarnock was closed production was transferred to Marquette in France.

MF combines were made in six plants, all six eventually closing. These were Toronto Canada, Batavia in USA, Manchester and Kilmarnock in the UK, Marquette in France and Eschwege in Germany. In 1964, a new combine plant opened at Brantford, Ontario, replacing the Toronto factory. This was to become one of the largest combine factories in the world. where the newly launched 410 and 510 combines were produced.

The 600s

The 600's were introduced as the MF 620 without the Multi Flow and the MF 625 with Multi Flow system, ending with the 625 Super 11. The '5' denotes a machine with Multi Flow. There were many design improvements over the old MH combines, the saddle grain tanks and re thresher were two of these and a top mounted engine instead of the under slung engines on the 780 and 788 models. High Inertia drums appeared with the MF 525 Super 11 and MF 625 and Quick Attach headers with the 510. Open bottom walkers appeared with the 400 and 500 series, but later Danish built MF combines returned to the closed bottoms. The Multi Flow system became available in 1969. The 520/525's had squarer styling compared to the earlier Massey models.

The 1970s- the 760

The 760 was launched in North America in 1971. A Series of paddle elevators replaced the feeder chain was introduced on the 760, which moved the grain from the table up the elevator. This was unique to MF at the time.

In June 1973, it was announced that Massey Ferguson would be launching a 'super jumbo' combine on the UK market in the next year or two, the MF 760 following field trials and market evaluation. It was claimed at the time to be the biggest combine ever made in North America, with 5ft wide and 22in diameter drum, with 24ft cutting widths, but in Europe these were 16, 18 or 20ft. Output was estimated to be in the region of 15-18 tons an hour, it was believed at the time that by 1980, there would be much more demand for jumbo size combines. Modifications were made for European conditions to cope with the heavier straw in the crops, including a bigger engine and still longer straw walkers.

In 1974, when the 760 was introduced in UK, it was the world's largest combine. It was built for the North American conditions, it was found to have limited capacity to separate grain from the straw in UK conditions. According to one source, over 400 Brantford built MF 750 and MF 760 combines came to the UK by mid 1978.

The 700 machines were due to be replaced by the updated 850 and 860 which were marketed in 1981.

The Power Flow table

Experiments began in 1977 for the Power Flow header. MF had been testing a new header to replace the North American Canadian built headers which struggled to cope with the longer straw of British crops. Trials showed that grain separation improved if the whole crop was fed head first into the drum. Oilseed rape was becoming popular at this time, which sped on the development of this header.

The Power Flow header was a major innovation in combine technology launched in 1977 by MF and still in use today in tables up to 9m wide. It was developed by a team led by Massey Fergusons chief combine engineer, Mr Jim McNaught, and first used on the MF 750 and MF 760 combines. It features a heavy strong rubberised conveyor belt with moulded ribs along their length, which 'powers' the crop away from the cutter bar to the intake auger on the table. Situated between the cutter bar and the auger, the belt took the crop away from the knives, to the auger in a head up direction. Four rollers kept the belts tensioned and running. It has the advantage in ensuring a more consistent and even flow of many different crops in any conditions, and also ensuring more crop arrives head first at the drum, which improves threshing and separation performance.

In 1979, the Power Flow table was offered on the 525 and 626 Super 11, the 750 and 760 in cutting widths of 14, 16 and 18ft. By 1984, MF were experimenting with a Dronningborg table mounted on Canadian built 865's which needed a trunk extension to join it to the combine and an additional rubber feed paddle to feed the crop to the drum. A new and improved Power Flow table was offered on the Dronningborg combines in brown livery, on the 27, to 31 from 1985. This had more refined belts made from softer more flexible nitrile rubber using a moulded V belt system with the ribbing now bonded on, and was lighter, and also did not need the pitch roller adjustment as on the earlier models, and they were now available with a header reversing mechanism in the event of blockages.

MF FRENCH COMBINE PRODUCTION
Production took place in Marquette from 1953 to 1985.

After the Massey Harris and Ferguson merger, production in France and Germany began. Today, combines are produced in Brazil, USA and Italy.

Smaller combines for the smaller farmer were made in France and sold in the UK. These included the MF 307 which was launched for the 1975 season replacing the 187 and the 487 Special was replaced by a restyled 506. The 307 was larger and came with a Perkins 77hp A4.236 engine, larger grain tank and hydrostatic instead of mechanical drive. A 8ft 6in model cost £5,870 and a 10ft cut model cost £6,020 in 1975. The 506 cost £7,750 for a 12ft cut model, or £7,670 for a 10ft Quick Attach table.

In 1984, six new medium size combine models were launched, the MF 845, 835, 830, 825, 805 and 800. The 800 to 835 were more powerful and improved versions of the existing 500 and 600 series at that time. These

combine models had been launched with options of Power flow and New Profile headers, as a result of an investment of £6.5 million by MF at their Marquette factory in France which was due for completion in 1984.

THE CANADIAN COMBINES MF 855 AND 865
MF acquired the design technology and manufacturing rights for the White rotary model. Some of these made their way to European markets.

Canada produced the larger end of the combine range for MF up until the 1980's. The MF 860 and 850 were launched in North America in 1981, these Brantford built 800 Series were announced in the UK in 1981 for the 1982 harvest. The 865 and 855 were available in North America from 1985. The 865 and 855 were launched in N America in 1985, but were available in Europe from late 1981 for the 1982 harvest. Some Canadian built MF combines are still seen in the UK, the 760, 755, 765, 750, 855, 865 and the 860 which arrived a year or two after the 865 was available.

The flagship 865 was the top of the range of the 800 series. It had a 184hp engine and 15% more capacity than the 765 which it replaced. It used a cascade separator system that had a beater to strip away the grain from the straw as it fell from the end of the walkers. The Cascade Separator system followed on from the Multi Flow, except that the rotor was placed higher up in the straw hood so that the combine was less likely to block up when the combine stopped forward motion and straw continued to be ejected from the machine. The 865 had an 18ft cut, and was the end of the Massey conventional combine production in Canada, apart from a 8680, not seen in UK. Some MF combines were made by Claas in the late 1980's to early 1990's, these were badged MF and sold as 8400's. These did not sell in the UK, but were sold in Canada to replace the 800 series there.

MF ROTARY MODEL
The MF 8590 rotary model had a 248hp V8 engine with 14ft long rotor and 18ft , 20ft or 22ft header and was demonstrated in the UK in 1986. The machine filled a gap in the MF combine range, but it was withdrawn from the market. It would have made MF the only manufacturer to offer both

high capacity Rotary and conventional combines. A decision was taken to proceed with expanding the Dronningborg range upwards.

END OF BRANTFORD

MF fell on hard times in the 1980's, along with most machinery manufacturers to a lesser extent, due to falling sales and low farm commodity prices in the US.

Following a reorganisation, the Brantford plant was sold off. Massey Combines Corporation which was then formed went into receivership in 1988. MF had experimented with developing a rotary range, the TX 801 to TX 804 and TX 903, but these never came to the UK and were shelved.

THE 1990S MF BECOMES PART OF AGCO.

AGCO was formed in 1990, (Allis Gleaner Corporation), and is based in Georgia USA. AGCO agricultural products are sold through four core brands Fendt, Challenger, Valtra and Massey Ferguson. Their main product at that time was the Gleaner machine which was built in Independence, Kansas City at the old Allis Chalmers factory. AGCO purchased the North American distribution rights for Massey Ferguson, White and New Idea in 1993 and Massey Fergusons world wide holdings the following year. Their initial impacts on MF were the purchase of Dronningborg and the Randers factory in Denmark, and also in 1996 AGCO bought the agricultural equipment division of the Maxion company in Brazil, giving MF 100% ownership of the Santa Rosa factory. At this time Maxion was licensee for AGCO's Massey Ferguson tractors and combines and also manufactured combines under the Ideal brand. AGCO also bought back the rotary combine from Western Combines Corporation.

MF CONNECTIONS WITH DRONNINGBORG

Denmark had become the main MF combine production centre. MF became involved with Dronningborg in 1984, which had been making their own models. Since the closure of the MF British, French and Australian factories in the 1980's, some MF combines were made in Denmark. AGCO, by then owners of MF, bought Dronningborg outright in 1997.

Following an agreement with Dronningborg, MF European combines were built by them to MF specifications.

MF AND DRONNINGBORG

In 1985, MF introduced the Dronninborg range - the 24, 27, 29 and 31 combines, badged as MF, the old MF 800 series apart from the largest model, and Dronningborg 7000 and 8000 models were phased out. The smaller model MF 24 was sold as an entry model. All had hydrostatic steering and electronic monitoring. By 1996, the MF 30 and 40 series combines had a curved glass screen for the cab, a new style multi function lever to operate the hydrostatic transmission and table controls. Datavision 11 was added, enabling the operator to control all machine settings through a computer as well as an on screen handbook for maintenance and monitoring of combine functions. The MF 24, the 170hp MF 31XP, and the MF 34 to the 220hp 38 models with the Datavision monitoring system were made in Finkudar, known internally in MF as the Randers factory, by Dronningborg and badged as MF models.

The MF 38 was a hydrostatic machine with header controls operated with switches, Chaff spreaders were added in 1991 on some models, and the following year, the 36 and 40 models were made into higher hp versions of the 34 and 38.

ADVENT OF ELECTRONICS - MF 38

The MF 38 was introduced and replaced the MF 865. Made in Denmark by Dronningborg in 1988, it had computerised performance monitoring and information systems, including a complete operators manual, which was displayed on a TV screen in an air conditioned cab. It also featured a cruise control unit designed to give optimum output by increasing and decreasing forward speed related to crop density and cylinder load. It was also possible to link the monitoring system with satellites in space to create a yield map of the field to assist with crop management.

MF CONNECTIONS WITH SAMPO ROSENLEW

From 1980 to around 2005, MF combines were marketed by Sampo Rosenlew of Finland. These were the result of a supply agreement between MF, AGCO and Sampo Rosenlew. They were smaller combines highly successful in the wetter conditions of Scandinavian countries.

The MF 330 and 430 were made from 1982-1984. The 430 being the largest of the MF models built by Sampo in Finland and joined the existing MF 240 and MF 440 for smaller farms.

By 1989, Massey Ferguson of Kenilworth Warwickshire was marketing the MF 8 Plot model, MF 16, and 20 in the UK which were made by Sampo Rosenlew, from the mid to late 1980's. Other models manufactured by Sampo Rosenlew in Finland included the MF 22, MF 23, MF 25 and MF 26 which were sold under the MF brand name but did not come to the UK. These were made from 1991 to 2002 and the MF 28 was made from 1987 to 2002. MF badged Sampo combines are still made and sold in Scandinavia. Later MF models made by Sampo were the MF 7238, 2035, 2045, 2065 and 2085 made from 2003.

PLOT COMBINES BUILT FOR MF.

Some MF Plot combines appeared in the UK, some of these were made in Finland for MF and AGCO by Sampo. The MF 8 XP Plot combine was used for experimental farms and the MF 8 was made as a plot and as a conventional combine. Coleman Engineering plot division of Dunmow Essex imported two Sampo Plot models in 1989, the 130 and 580.

THE 2000S

By 2000, the 30/40 series were replaced by the 7200 series, with seven models from the 7250 to the largest, the 7276. They featured the standard Autoglide Automatic table control system, but the MF Powerflow and Freeflow tables were still options, green emission compliant engines made by Valmet of Finland, with optional rotary separator. Precision farming systems appeared in the form of MF Fieldstar for yield monitoring and mapping.

Cerea models appeared from Dronningborg's Randers factory, with the larger models having eight walkers. In 2002 four Cerea models appeared from Dronningborg's Randers factory, the MF7256, 7272, 7274 and 7278 with hill side AL versions, with the large models having eight walkers. By 2005, the Cerea range comprised only 7274 and 7278 models.

In 2002 the first Activa model the 7242 appeared. By 2005, this was dropped and the Activa range comprised the 7244, 7245 and 7246. Current Activa models as at 2009 consist of the 7240 to 7246 and 7247, available in S and AL versions, and ranging from 176hp to 275hp. In 2005, Beta mid range models comprised the 7260, 7260AL-4, 7270 and 7270AL-4. The current line up for the 2010 harvest is 7260 and 7270 with S and AL versions, ranging in hp from 275 to 335hp.

The latest, the largest MF combines, the eight walker 378hp Sisu engine Centora 7280 and the Sisu 413hp 7282 , were demonstrated in the UK in 2009. These have standard Powerflow headers of 9.1m for the first time, and replace the Cerea range.

SAMPO ROSENLEW

Sampo Rosenlew are based at Pori, Finland, where the machines are designed and manufactured. The company have had close ties with MF and Deutz Fahr in the past. Sampo Rosenlew also purchased the Aktiv combine company.

Their main product is the combine harvester manufactured in two series, the 2000 series and the high capacity 3000 series.

SAMPO ROSELEW AND SAME DEUTZ FAHR

In 2003-04, Sampo reached an agreement with Same Deutz Fahr to manufacture and sell combines. The Deutz-Fahr 55 combine series introduced at Agritechnica 2003, is based on Sampos 3000 series. The original idea was shelved when Deutz Fahr moved their manufacturing of the 5 straw walker Top Liner to Croatia. Deutz Fahr also phased out the 5 walker Top Liner combines replacing them with the 55 series comprising five and six walker machines available from 2004 harvest.

Rosenlew developed threshing machines in the 1860's and since the 1950's self propelled combines. Sampo Ltd bought out the combine business when some of the Rosenlew operations came to an end, others such as the combine business became independent companies. With the export business in mind, the heavy duty 3000 series was introduced in 2001 and the twin separator TS model 3085 was added in 2003. The flagship 6 walker machine has a beater drum mounted in front of the threshing drum similar to John Deere's T series and the Claas APS System.

The new pre cylinder enabled wider cutting tables and larger grain tanks to be used. In the early 1920's Sampo was adopted as the brand of the threshing machine. The first combine at the Porin works in 1957, a Self propelled 657LP model, was nicknamed 'Grandma Sampo'.

The 792LP nicknamed the Grandpa Sampo followed in 1961.

In 1971, Sampo became Sampo Rosenlew and two new models were launched, the SR 25 and 35.

In 1973, the 310 and 360 appeared with 1700 litre grain tanks and 54hp engine.

In 1978 to 1997, the 500 Series with 2.7m to 3.1m headers and 87cm wide drum were marketed. These had 64 to 87hp Valmet engines and straw walkers increased from three to four.

By 1971, the first medium size combine appeared, the SR40 with a 3m/10ft header and 106cm wide drum, powered by a 82hp Valmet engine. This was followed by the SR 400 range in 1977 which came with an optional cab.

In 1982, an agreement with Massey Ferguson enabled Sampo to market the SR600 under red MF livery as the MF 430 and in 1985, the MF 20.

The 2000 Series was launched in 1990, replacing the long lived 600 Series. The drum was now 112cm wide. The 2055 had a 6 cylinder 120hp engine and 3300 litre grain tank with cutting widths of 3.4m to 4.2m.

The SR 2075TS was launched in 1996, with its longer length due to the pre cylinder, TS Twin Separation, engine power could be increased to 185hp and grain tank capacity rose to 4600 litres. A pre separator was placed in front of the drum. Header width was 4.8m.

The SR 2045 and 2050 followed the 2055. These were both 4 cylinder models of 87hp and 100hp. Top of the range was the 2060 140hp model with 4200 litre grain tank. The following year a five straw walker combine appeared, the 2065.

In 2001, the 3000 Series with 1.34m wide drum was launched. The first two models, the 3045 and 3065 had six walkers and 1.34m wide drum, with options of 175hp, 200hp and 220hp engines. The largest engine size rose to 276hp. Cutting widths were 4.2m and 5.7m. In 2003, the 3085 Twin Separation model was launched, which meant that the grain tank size could be increased to 8100 litres and the header width to 6.3m.

The Sampo combine range has been available in the UK since 1994, but has not been actively marketed until 2008. The small plot combine has been available and marketed since 1989.

The models sold are the five walker 2045 and 2065, the five walker with pre threshing drum 2085, and new for 2010 the 2095 combine. These use Sisu engines from 120hp to 210hp, with headers from 3.45m to 4.8m. The six walker machines comprise the 3065 and the 3085 combines with header widths from 5.1m to 6.3m and Sisu engines from 210hp to 276hp. They are marketed by Trials Equipment (UK) Ltd.

CLAAS

No book about the development of the combine harvester is complete without mention of this enterprising German company.

Franz Claas was born in March 1859 in Clarholz near Gutersloh Germany. His Father Heinrich Claas was a farmer. Franz trained as a vet but from an early age showed signs of technical ability, he made his own lathes. He began making farming equipment in the 1880's, and learnt the basis of his engineering skills and forging techniques from a local blacksmith. At his home farm, Heerde near Harsewinkel, Franz started making centrifuges for the mechanical skimming of milk and was registered as a business in 1902 as the 'Centrifugenfabrik Franz Claas'. There was also a contracting business alongside the farm and he made threshing machines. Franz tuned to making straw trussers, which had begun to appear in England in the 1900's, and was one of the first to build a trusser which fitted to the threshing machines.

Franz had four sons, Bernhard, August, Franz and Theo. August born in 1887 went on a mechanical apprenticeship and founded the Claas company in Clarholtz in 1913, repairing and manufacturing straw binders, with brothers Franz and Bernhard joining him later. The company became known as Gebruder Claas in 1914. During the war, trading ceased, but after the brothers returned from service in the war, business was resumed. The foundations of the Claas company began, in 1919, the Claas brothers bought an old brickworks in Harsewinkel where their business was established, and the company headquarters and factory have remained there ever since. August continued to make straw binders, and later fertiliser spreaders followed and straw balers. The straw binders were fitted with the improved Claas knotter with an upper lip, with which he had been experimenting. This was his first patent awarded by the DLG German Farming Association. and was the turning point in the success of this company. This put Claas on the map worldwide and is still used as the company's trademark today. Production of other machines followed, Claas was the first company to make a pick up baler which was exported to New Zealand, Canada and the rest of Europe.

However, it was the development of the combine harvester for European conditions which gave Claas the breakthrough.

A unique factor also is that this company is still today family owned, and one of the few agricultural companies to remain in family hands rather than merged with multi business concerns. It has been remarked that there is a special family bond that kept the Claas brothers together, and even to this day, there is a high degree of loyalty at all levels to the family and their company. There is a team spirit rarely seen in large corporate companies. This is a foundations tone for its success, and combined with a will to succeed, business acumen and persistence are reasons explain why this company is one of the survivors, while so many companies ceased trading over the years.

The four Claas brothers each had their own function in the company from managing tool making and factory equipment, management of the business to personnel management and commercial development. Helmut, eldest son of August, inherited his Fathers entrepreneurial skills and entered the family business at an early age in 1958, devoting himself to engineering and product development. He had attended Hanover Technical University to study mechanical engineering studies after which he went to Paris to the Grande Ecole Nationale d'Agriculture. Along with his younger brothers, Reinhold, Walter and Gunther, they continue to pursue the goal of running the company as a family business.

In 2000, responsibility was transferred to the next generation, with Helmut's daughter Cathrina.

THE MDB
The first combine.

The first attempts were not successful. In 1931, Dr August Claas and Mr Brenner, a designer at Harsewinkel devised a combine which fitted around a 30hp Lanz Bulldog tractor, but it was not a success, and the idea was dropped when the first trailed combine was made in 1936. It had a 6ft front mounted cutter bar Feed chains transported the grain with the ears hanging downwards alongside the tractor. Behind this, a vertical threshing drum of 35cm diameter was fitted to separate the grain. Mowing, tying and assembling sheaves the old way was all done away with, the combine undertook these steps in one operation. It was demonstrated at Bielefeld later in 1931, and the prototype was also tested in the UK by the institute of Engineering at Oxford, mounted on a Marshall tractor. It did not impress the representatives of other reaper manufacturers present in Germany. Another attempt was made to interest Lanz, at a demonstration near Zweibrucken, but this was not a success either, this design was soon abandoned.

After this, Claas continued on their own to develop a combine. August Claas and Professor Vormfelde from the Agricultural Engineering Institute at Bonn University went to Paris and Chicago to pick up ideas, looking at trailed combines.

Development of a new pull type combine began in 1934, resulting in the first combine harvester in Europe, the MDB.

The first Claas combine was exhibited at the Imperial Food Production Exhibition in 1934 at Erfurt.

In 1936, the trailed and pto driven Claas MDB-Mah-Dresch-binder, (Mower-Thresher-binder) became the first mass produced combine harvester designed for European conditions. It was a pure transverse flow combine, with a 7ft cutter bar similar to a binder, fitted on the right, requiring a tractor with 45hp output for the drive with a pto. The crop was conveyed through ninety degrees for threshing and separation. The grain was fed to the drum on a moving mat similar to the binders. A chain fed the straw around the threshing drum and threw it onto the straw walkers, which were wider than the American version of trailed combines at the time, in order to cope with European harvests. The concave had a large wrap angle. It had a two stage cleaning system, like the stationery threshers, with a diswner and air suction, and the second with an air blast. Grain was filled into sacks on a bagging platform. It was advertised with an output of 1.5 to 2.5 ton an hour. The first machine with a serial number was delivered to a farm for the 1936 harvest in East Germany. It was also tested in UK, and the sixth one built was sent to Scotland. One thousand had been made by 1941. In 1943, production ceased due to being forced to turn to military production.

After the Second World War, the combine harvester was turned into an every day tool, thanks to the pull type Super model launched in 1946. More than 65,000 units were sold by 1978. A Super was found in the factory by English occupational forces and confiscated and sent to England. However, it was of so little interest that no one thought it worth producing there. Later the test results re appeared and an import licence was made available so the confiscated machine eventually opened the door to exports to England. Following trials of the Super by the NIAE at Askam Bryan, the Board of Trade requisitioned eleven of them under war reparations and had them shipped to the UK. The existing Claas agent, D Lorant of Radlett in Hertfordshire declined to handle them, so the eleven machines were offered to J Mann and Son of Saxham in Suffolk. The connection was made because Manns were listed as importors of Lanz tractors from Germany.

Bill Mann from Saxham in Suffolk imported the first Super trailed harvesters to Britain in 1947. The Super was built on the same lines as the MDB with a cross-flow conveyor, transverse threshing and longitudinal separations system. Soon, large numbers were imported to England following two years of harvest trials and modifications made. It was then the combine with the highest performance in the world. Like the MDB, the crop was cut with the cutter bar on the right hand side of the machine. It then flowed to the drum via a conveyor. A right angle flow principle was adopted, the crop being transported sideways and then lengthways. A tractor giving 35hp at the pto was required to run it. It had a 2.10m cutting width with a straw press fitted as standard.

The smaller Super Junior appeared in 1953 following on from the success of the Super, with a 5ft 6in cutter bar and 50in wide drum with six rasp bars, powered by a tractor producing 25hp at the PTO. Later in 1955, the Super 500, replaced the Super, it was a larger machine which came as a tanker or bagger model.

The Super family was continuously improved, grain tanks eventually replaced the bagging platform and choppers replaced the straw press. At this time, auxiliary engines were added to the combines enabling smaller tractors to be used for the threshing.

In 1959, the 7ft cut Super Automatic was launched, so called because it had its own hydraulic system which enabled the tractor driver to control the combine with a hydraulic control unit, to vary cutting functions and reel height control. It was pulled by a 35hp tractor and it could harvest 3½ tons an hour. The Junior Automatic replaced the Junior in 1960. The Automatics were the first one man Claas trailed combines, the Super needed three men. They were the last Claas combines with the right angle layout.

The Garant was the last of the pull type combines launched in 1967, but with a straight line crop flow.

The Super pull type combine were still being produced in large numbers, but during the fifties and sixties, pull-type machines were being replaced by self propelled. The Harsewinkel team supported by August Claas personally, developed a self propelled machine called the Hercules, with front mounted cutter bar, which was launched in 1952, and was produced until 1963. However the name was changed to the SF, when problems emerged with registration of the name.

Hercules had already been registered at the Hercules Motor Corporation of Canton, Ohio. It was aimed at farmers and contractors and also for the export market, and was supplied with a bagging platform or grain tank, with or without the mounted baler. The cutting width was 2.40m, hydraulically operated. It had a 1.25m threshing drum and four straw walkers, powered by a 56hp Perkins diesel engine in UK, later a 60hp was fitted. The self propelled machines were all designed with a straight crop flow. Later models, such as the Matador, Senator, Protector were based on a similar design to the SF. Farmers in Britain at the time did not have much choice in the way of self propelled combines, many would have had a 780. The Marshall E9 did not last long, and the 726 was in use. The new 780 in 1953 was cheaper than Claas and still popular, but to many, it did not match up to the quality of German steel and bearings, and lacked the designs of the Claas engineers. This is still true in many cases today. The SF had a number of innovations, the hydraulic table and reel lift, and manually operated variable speed drives for travel and drum speed, whereas although the 780 had a variable sped traction drive, the drum speed on the 780 could only be altered by changing sprockets and still had electric table lift. Manns launched the new SF at the Royal Show in July 1953, and subsequently imported thirteen of the SF combines in 1953, they were known in the UK as SP for Self Propelled. Due to teething problems,

the SP machines were recalled to Saxham at the end of the season.

After modifications, Manns sold 80 SP combines for the 1954 harvest which had headers of 8ft 10ft and 12ft and a choice of Austin Newage or Perkins engines. The SP was re launched in 1955 at the DLG show in Munich and the SP name was dropped and reverted to the German SF name. Manns imported 112 of these improved machines for the 1955 harvest, some in tanker form and just over half still as baggers. These were redesigned completely, one of the main features being that the hydraulic functions for the table, reel drum and road speeds were all controlled with one lever in a six gate quadrant beneath the steering wheel. This hydraulic gate continued on the Matador and Senator models. Sales continued to rise annually, the SF stood the test of wet harvests and laid crops, and continued in production until 1963, the last version was renamed the SFB in UK, and was sold as a cheaper version for the smaller farmer when the Matador first appeared in 1960. The SFB had a Perkins engine and wider tyres. These proved to be a very popular combine at the time, Manns sold 1500 during 1963, although by now more models were appearing in the market place from Ransomes, Claeys and Allis-Chalmers giving UK farmers greater choice.

Claas also experimented with a self propelled combine for use by smaller farmers, which became known as the Huckepack.

The Huckepack was displayed at the DLG exhibition in Hanover in 1956, which was a hybrid SP combine which also could be adapted to use implements like a tractor. It had a 2.10m header, three straw walkers, bagger platform with a straw press at the rear and was produced from 1957. A forerunner of the Xerion tractor, the prime mover was driven by a 12hp diesel engine and the combine unit had an industrial VW 34hp engine. However production was discontinued in 1960 due to lack of sales, possibly due to inadequate engine power, or unavailability of quick coupling systems for the hydraulics, electrical equipment and the pto.

The Europa, a smaller model was launched in 1958 and marketed for use all over Europe, hence the name Europa, and was aimed at smaller farmers who had still continued to use stationery threshing machines. A three walker combine, it has a 2.10m 7ft wide cutter bar, and a feature was the very long crop dividers. It came as a bagger or tanker model with the option of a straw chopper behind the straw press. And was powered by a 45hp Perkins diesel engine or 38hp VW industrial engine, with an 800mm wide drum, though some earlier models had a Mercedes Benz engine. The drum diameter was 450mm, this was retained on Claas combines for many years to come. It was an advanced machine for its day, having an automatic cutting height system, achieved by a sensing method with springs fitted to the lift cylinders.

The Columbus followed in 1958, which was the same as the Europa except for a smaller 1.80m cutter bar and a 29hp VW industrial engine with the option of a 34hp diesel. This stayed in production until 1970.

The Mecur, known as Mercury in the UK was launched in 1963. It had four walkers, but a narrower drum width it filled the gap between the larger Matador and the Columbus and Europa. These combines were extremely up to date by contemporary standards with features such as hydraulic cutter bar and reel control, and hydraulically controlled drive variator.

The Matador appeared in 1961 to meet the demands for higher capacity combines, it was a much larger combine with four walkers, 1250 drum width and six cylinder Perkins 87hp engine, and was claimed to be the largest combine at the time outside the USSR. The successor to the SF, the Gigant or Giant which evolved from the Matador, had a 12ft cut and cost £2,912 in 1964. It was aimed at larger farmers, which the SF could no longer cater for, and had cutter bars up to 20ft and the option of power steering. The smaller version, the 10ft Matador Standard, also with four straw walkers, was launched in 1962/1963 and had a 4 cylinder 62hp engine and replaced the SFB. Both had larger grain tanks which by now were standard, with the straw press on the back being an option, and the engine was now fitted behind the grain tank. On the Matador series around 1964, the silver grey colour changed to Astral Green livery.

A succession of new models followed, the Comet, Cosmos, Consul, Mercator and Senator.

The Senator in 1966 marked a complete change both in appearance and colour to previous combines. With larger outer panels, and a new Claas logo, it was painted a leaf green colour. It had four walkers, 10.5 diesel engine and all were now tanker combines, with the bagging platforms discontinued. Headers were 3.0m to 4.20m. The smaller Protector was

launched in 1968 whith 4 and 6 cylinder engines of 68hp, and from 2.6m headers. The Mercator in 1967 replaced the Senator, now having additional numbers after the name, 50 to 85 to denote different sizes in the range, but in the UK the Senator name was kept instead of the Mercator used in Germany. In 1974, the ISS system was launched for the following harvest and was featured on the larger Senator 85. The ISS system featured one or two agitator tines on cranks working immediately above the straw walkers to reduce density of material. These agitated the straw, lifting it so that the straw could flow better, and grains remaining in the straw could fall through onto the returns floor underneath the walkers. This system was also fitted to the Dominator range and became one of the classic Claas features on their combines. The Senators remained on the market until the early 1980's, they appeared in the German price list for the last time in 1981 for the following harvest. The first basic cabs appeared on the Senator and Mercator models, in the UK, made by Cabcraft or Lambourne.

To cater for the smaller farmers, several models were introduced, bearing the same leaf green and styling as the Senator, but with a side mounted engine. The Consul and Cosmos were introduced in 1967 and the Comet and Corsar followed, all derived from the larger Senator, but these only remained in production for three years, and were not very popular in the UK. All had the Claas 450mm drum diameter but had varying drum widths and cutter bar widths from 1.80 to 3.0m, and were offered with different engine choices. The Consul had four walkers and 68hp engine, apart from the Consul which had four straw walkers, the others all had three. These were replaced by the three straw walker Compact 20 and a five straw walker Compact 25, which unlike their predecessors, were purpose built, with the aim of providing an economic small combine for farms with small fields. They had VW industrial engines from 24hp to 34hp, and were phased out by the 1981/1982 season, with the last model in the range, the Compact 30 with a 53hp engine. These three models had an unusual feature in that a fold-up straw cowl enabled the driver to check and clean the walkers and sieves, despite the low height of the combine.

The next major landmark was the Dominator 5 series in 1970, and the Dominator 6 series with new styling in 1978.

The five straw walker Dominator 80 with 105hp engine in 1970 was the first combine to have hydrostatic drive, which was optional on this model. This was followed by the six walker Dominator 100 with 170hp engine and standard hydrostatic transmission, and the 85 in 1974. This was the first of a long rang e of combines and one of the most popular sold by this company. In 1974, the Retromat system was launched for the 1975 harvest, and became available as a factory fitted extra only on Dominator 85 models with the mechanical transmission, which allows the combine to be put into reverse without shifting gears in order to make turning easier. A hillside version, the Dominator 85H was developed in 1978, but was not a big success, due to its extra cost, and as far as I know, few were sold in Germany or the UK. The compensation was achieved by four hydraulic cylinders, regulated by an electrical control unit attached to the front axle. This maintains the combines centre of gravity across steep slopes. A new feature was the situation of the engine directly behind the cab, with the grain tank at the rear. The reason for his was that Claas claimed that it enabled shorter drives to be used to the threshing drum which took the most power. The Dominator 85 was the first to have a pre-selected cutting height option, the header returned to a pre selected height automatically after headland turns. The Dominator '6' models launched in 1978, were the first to have a comfort cab integrated into the combine, together with function monitors for monitoring speeds of the straw walkers, grain and returns elevators, and electronic throughput controls for losses over the walkers and sieves. The Dominator '8' series followed in early 1980's, with the smaller 48 and 38 and later the larger capacity 78, 88, 98 and 108 were launched in 1985 for the 1986 season, replacing the 6 series. The 221hp 108SL was the top of the range with a Mercedes engine and optional 3D sieves. List price in 1985 for a Dominator 98SL was £55,550. These came in the mechanical ground drive S version, or SL-Super Luxe with hydrostatic drive. They featured the multi function control lever, and also an on-board information system providing visual displays of travel speed, operating hours, shaft rpm, and also the cabs now became air conditioned and had heating. The Contour cutter bar control appeared on the '8' series, where by the cutter bar could be run with ground contact, and oil bath knife drive replaced the wobble box type. This was achieved by linking the automatic cutting height pre-selection with a ground pressure control. This was later followed by the Auto Contour cutter bar.

Claas enters Rotary market

In 1981, Claas added a new separating system, the CS version of the 250hp Dominator 116. This retained the drum and concave but a set or rotary separators and concaves replaced the straw walkers. Grain passing through the 8 concaves passed to a standard sieve and fan arrangement.

The forced rotor separation of the Axial Flow combines imported from America by IH in the 1970's produced high performances in dry conditions but these machines could not cope with the wet green straw often found in the UK. Claas instead of following this idea developed the "Cylinder System" on the Dominator 116CS introduced in 1981 for the following harvest, with eight separation cylinders behind the drum with concaves underneath. The cylinders then force fed the straw to the straw hood. Due to the higher cost of the machine, more complex parts requiring more maintenance and inadequate engine power, this combine did not sell in large numbers, however it was still produced until 1995. In order to distinguish them from the Dominator straw walker combines, later Dominator CS models were renamed the Commandor family in 1986, with the Commandor 115CS being added to the existing Dominator 112CS, 114CS and 116CS. The top of the range Commandor 228 model which followed in 1992 had a 330hp engine, and cutting widths up to 7.50m. The Auto Contour system was introduced on the Commandor CS in 1990. In addition to difficulties cutting on steep slopes, the wider headers now being used posed problems on slopes. On the up hill side of a slope, wider cutter bars tended to lift up from the ground, while the lower side drive wheels would sink into the ground from extra heavy weight. As a result, the Claas Auto Contour system was devised to resolve this problem. With this system, the cutter bar follows the ground laterally and in the direction of travel, giving a uniform stubble height.

By 2000, most of the Dominator series had been replaced by the Medion series.

Sperry New Holland was one of the first companies to alleviate hillside combining difficulties. They developed an automatic sieve box levelling control. The preparation pan, fans and sieves remained horizontal in relation to the ground. Also at this time, Claas produced the 3D dynamic slope compensation system where the upper sieve is given a side movement against the slope, so keeping the crop evenly distributed on the sieves up to a slope of 20%.

With the launch of the Dominator Mega range came the Claas APS (Accelerated Pre-Separation) system introduced for the 1993 harvest. Whereas other manufactures such as new Holland devised the Rotary Separator situated behind the impellor, to achieve greater separation inn conditions with green straw and higher yields now becoming common, Claas put in accelerator drum in front of the main threshing drum, which speeds up the crop flow before it enters the drum. Centrifugal forces in the threshing unit are improved, assisting early separation. The APS appeared on the Mega 208 and 218 and later on the other Mega models. The Dominator Mega Models were followed by Mega 11 202 to 218's in 1996. The Mega models had engine power from 235 to 270hp and cutter bars from 4.50m to 6.00m. Three smaller five straw walker models, the 202, 203 and 204 were launched the following year in 1994.

More Technology the Lexion

The CS combines were too complex with their eight cylinders. The solution was launched in 1995 for the 1996 harvest, with the first hybrid combine with Roto-Plus system, the Lexion 480. The conventional threshing system had been married with a pair of rotors fitted lengthways. The APS threshing system with the accelerator in front of the threshing drum, first launched on the Mega, was now retained on the Lexion, but the drum size was increased to 600mm giving a larger separation area. The straw impeller divides the crop into two streams and guides it onto the axial rotors which have spiral flights to feed the straw to the rear of the machine. High centrifugal forces enable a high forced separation to be achieved.

With this model came more sophistication, a new Vista cab, which had been launched on some of the later Mega series, the CEBIS-Claas-On-Board-Information-system, a computer which monitors all machine functions, and combine settings which can be undertaken electronically, plus systems such as yield mapping. The Vario Cutter bar which extended

500mm from the basic knife position for the rape harvest was introduced in 1998 on the Lexion range. This could be done from the cab, extending it by 200mm on the move or shortening it by 100mm.

Also, after nearly 60 years, Claas changed the 450mm diameter threshing drum to the larger 600mm drum, to increase separation area in the bigger combines. Other manufacturers had changed their drum sizes, Fahr from 460mm to 600mm, IHC from 460 to 560mm, John Deere to 610mm and MF at 560mm and New Holland were 600mm, claiming a larger drum gave more efficient threshing and less risk of crop wrapping. With header sizes up to 9m, and 400hp engines, the 480 was at the time the largest combine on the market. Other features are the quick coupling of header electric and hydraulic hoses with one plug and a new straw chopper built to distribute the straw over the wider cutting widths. Spreading fans under the chopper blow the straw and chaff over the full header width. In 1996 ready for the following harvest, the Lexion 405 - 460 straw walker machines were added, the 405 was discontinued before the other models, and the Lexion 470 hybrid with Roto Plus system was introduced as the last of the 400 series of Lexions in 2001, together with updated version of the walker models, which became known as the 460 and 430 Evolution. Other Evolution models were added to the walker range. The Lexion Montana hill side combine was introduced in 2002 for the 2003 season on the 470 and 430 models. The Evolution models featured Caterpillar engines using electronic fuel efficient technology, and the MSS Multi finger Separation System above the straw walkers instead of the ISS, before the launch of the new updated Lexion 500 series in 2003. By now GPS and Laser pilot were becoming common on the larger models. Laser Pilot was launched in 1999 on the Lexion.

Telematics launched in 2006 for 2007 harvest is another technological advance, to aid harvesting performance from today's latest combines. This uses an on board datalogger to record selected information copied from the CAN BUS system on the combine every 15 seconds. This data is converted and stored on a PCIMA card in the CEBIS monitor of the Lexion. Every 15 minutes an on board mobile telephone modem calls a data transfer station and downloads the machines data to the internet. This data can be accessed, viewed and analysed when required. A combine can be located using Google Earth, which shows a machines location in satellite photographs, location display tools can indicate if another trailer is required or how much crop is left to cut. Dealers can establish direct contact with a combine, telematics enables remote machine diagnostics, and combine data can be shared anonymously with other users to compare and adjust performance.

DANIA/DRONNINGBORG

In 1962, a Dania 7½ft self propelled tanker/bagger combine was marketed, with no number designation, it had a 4 cylinder Perkins diesel engine and it was said to awn and clean the grain better with its patented counterflow-up-draught cleaner and 2 way awner system, so making the grain pre cleaned ready for sale. It had a grain tank capacity of 40 bushels and estimated output was 1-2 acres an hour.

Dania was imported to the UK in 1966 and in that year, the Great Dane was marketed, made by Dronningborg Maskinfabrik of Randers Denmark, who had already had 60 years of experience of manufacturing grain and seed threshing equipment, supplied all over the world. This combine had a 10ft cut four straw walkers and Perkins 4 cylinder engine, it was capable of an output of 6 to 10 tons an hour. This had been tested in the UK and in Denmark and Norway and featured the Dania counterflow-up-draught cleaner and 2 way awner to remove weed seeds during threshing. In the 1960's, two pto driven Dania models were on the market, the 7ft 6in cut D750 which had an 18in drum diameter and grain tank of 58 bushels with bagging off platform available and the D600/500 which had cutting widths of 6ft or 5ft and 44 bushel grain tank with bagging off platform. Both had hydraulic table and reel control from tractor seat. Four self propelled models were available, the largest D-1800 with 13ft or 10ft header, 105hp 6 cylinder diesel engine, drum diameter of just over 22in and 63 bushel grain tank, the D-1500, D-1200 and smallest Self propelled D-900 with cutting width of 8ft drum diameter of 17in, 40 bushel grain tank and 50hp 4 cylinder diesel engine.

In November 1974, a new breed of Great Danes as they were known, were added to the Western/Dania range. The D2250 for above average acreages, with 14ft or 16ft cutting table, and 130hp engine and the D2600 for large acreages, with a 16ft, 18ft or 22ft table powered by a 206hp diesel engine with hydrostatic transmission was claimed by the importers, Western Machinery and Equipment to be one of the largest and most advanced combines in Europe. In 1974, the new 4 walker Dania D1600 filled the gap between the Western/Dania D1200 and the D2500, and came with 10 or 12ft cutting tables with 6 cylinder Perkins diesel 100hp engine and outputs were claimed to be up to 8½ tons an hour. The D1600 had a price of £7695 including a header trolley in 1974.

Dania model D900 was made at Randers in Denmark. This had an 8ft 4in cutting table, 62hp engine and 44in drum with 17in diameter. The D1900 and the 5 walker D-2250 had a 6 cylinder 130hp engine. The 5 walker D-2600 had a 8 Cylinder 200hp V8-540 engine, 140cm wide drum with diameter of 57.5cm.

The D8000 with 16ft or 18ft headers, 5 walkers and 136hp engine was the largest of the hydrostatic range comprising the D300, D4000 D7000. The D8000 had a 140cm wide 6 bar threshing drum with 45cm diameter. These were discontinued when MF began to make the MF 27, 29 and 31 models in Denmark.

MINNEAPOLIS-MOLINE

The G8 Minneapolis-Moline combine was British built and introduced by the UK importers Sale Tilney (Agricultural Ltd) of Wokingham, Berkshire, in 1946, whose premises were later bought by Allis-Chalmers. It was manufactured by an associate company, Minneapolis-Moline (England) Ltd and made at a factory in Dowlais in South Wales. The combine was produced in a choice of power units, either a four cylinder meadows or a Ford V8 engine. The MM G8 model was seen at the Royal Show in 1951, and a few were available for harvest that year in the UK. It was described as having excellent capacity and produced a good sample.

In 1947, the American designed Minneapolis Moline G2 trailed combine was made in Wales as the Minneapolis Moline G8 by Minneapolis Moline (UK) a company established by Sale Tilney (Agricultural) Ltd. Production of the G8 was transferred to Essendine Stamford in Lincolnshire, where it continued until 1950. The Essendine factory was then used by Allis-Chalmers where the American All Crop 60 was produced from May 1951 for ten years.

ALLIS CHALMERS-GLEANER

Like many of the other tractor and combine manufacturers such as Case, John Deere, and McCormick, the o-rigins of Allis-Chalmers go back to the first half of the nineteenth century. The Gleaner Combine Harvester Corporation of Missouri was one of the pioneers of early combines in the 1920's, along with another American firm, Advance-Rumely Thresher Company of La Porte, Indiana. Both became part of Allis Chalmers. The predecessor to Gleaner, Decker and Seville had supplied millstones for flour mills. A few years later in the 1850's, Edward Allis bought Decker and Seville, following a period of depression in the USA. Edward P Allis expanded into steam engines and saw mills. In 1901, Fraser and Chalmers, a steel and mining retort manufacturer from Chicago and two other companies called Gates Iron Works from Chicago and Dickson Manufacturing Company in Pennsylvania merged, forming the Allis-Chalmers Manufacturing Company. After the merger, Allis made waterwheels, sawmills and grindstones and later steam engines in the Milwaukee area of Wisconsin. Allis-Chalmers entered into the farm equipment business in 1914 during World War One. By 1913, Allis-Chalmers was making tractors, which expanded after the First World War. Allis-Chalmers began importing to the UK in 1932, opening an office in London, and a warehouse at Totton, near Southampton. After the Second World War, Allis relocated to Essendine, near Stamford, where Minneapolis-Moline stored their tractors. This site was used to store the trailed All Crop 60 combines.

As a result of the Allis company producing the Allis All Crop trailed combine, the end of the prairie machines was in sight. The All Crop was lighter and more compact and more suited to the American Mid West farmers. and was probably the first of a new breed of compact combines with a 5ft cutter bar, and straight line feed using a drum the same width as the cutter bar.

The Allis All Crop 60 had been launched in America in 1935. The original fore runner to the All Crop 60 was built in America, at La Porte in Indiana, where it was introduced in 1936. Imports from the USA began soon after the company established the distribution depot in 1936 at Totten. The improved American All Crop 60 harvester replaced the original All Crop harvester and was launched in 1940 and continued in production until 1952, some of which appeared in British harvest fields in 1941. Available in Britain by the 1950's the Allis All Crop 60 was a 5ft trailed machine, driven by a 25hp petrol or Vaporising oil engine, with the same drum width and concave with a rubber faced beater bar. As the crop left the drum, it turned through a right angle on to the sieves and straw rack, before the grain was elevated to a grain tank or bagging platform. The trailed All Crop 60 was the first combine produced at the Allis-Chalmers British factory at Essendine in Linclonshire. Production began on the British version of the All Crop 60 in May 1951at Essendine This was an exact duplicate of the American All Crop, using a petrol or vaporizing-oil engine which developed about 25hp. The engines were also made at Essendine. Production aims for the Essendine factory in 1951 were 500 units for the home market and about 1000 for export. The list price in August 1951 for the Allis-Chalmers Model 60 was £650. This model remained in production until 1960. It had a 5ft cut with a 5ft wide cylinder and the mechanism was engine driven apart from the reel which was adjusted by means of a rope from the tractor driver's seat.

In 1953, Allis-Chalmers purchased the Gleaner (Baldwin) Harvester Corporation, of Missouri Kansas, and acquired its self propelled combine designs. The following year Allis-Chalmers Great Britain Ltd tested an American Model A Gleaner Baldwin combine in England and Scotland. This had a Hercules QLXD six cylinder engine. In 1957 forty of these in basic form were imported into the UK to be assembled at Essendine, with quick-detach headers, and were fitted with British engines, either Perkins

P6 diesels, or Austin-Newage six cylinder petrol/TVO units. These were in the silver livery of the American Gleaner models, some modifications were made for the UK market.

The British version of the Model A combine , the Model EA Gleaner, was made at Essendine from 1958-1962, with threshing mechanism modifications being made to suit British harvesting conditions. Using Perkins or Austin engines, these had three-speed gearboxes, three straw walkers, and came with a choice of 10ft to 12ft headers, and were now in orange livery. In 1959, they were offered with a 8ft 6in header and four speed gearbox.

The Model C Gleaner was made at Essendine in 1962. It was based on the American version launched in 1960, and was a larger and heavier version of the smaller Model A, having a larger grain separation area and four straw walkers. It had a six cylinder Perkins diesel engine and 10ft or 12ft headers, and was made until 1964.

The Model A Super Gleaner was made from 1962-1964, with the first harvest being in 1963. This was modified from the first ES Gleaner due to the damp European harvesting conditions, it had a greater separation area and longer straw walkers. Engines used were either Perkins or BMC-Newage petrol/TVO. The straw walker hood was raised giving more separation area.

Super A Gleaner

Made from 1964-1971, it was launched at the 1964 Smithfield show and had a new appearance, with new sheet metal work giving it a longer and lower profile. It was powered by a Perkins 6.305 engine with three speed gearbox and the fuel tank was repositioned. Improvements were made to the grain tank unloading auger in later models and in 1968, it had a four cylinder Perkins engine.

Super C Gleaner

This ran alongside the Super A Gleaner, launched also in 1964, it had a larger grain tank, with larger elevators and unloading auger, but other features and improvements were the same. It had the same Perkins 6.305 engine and three speed gear box. The control panel was redesigned.

Model 5000

This was the last Allis-Chalmers British combine built and sales did not take off. Production ceased after the Bamford takeover of Allis in 1971.

With a new appearance, it was made from 1968-1971, following tests during the 1967 and 1968 harvests, but remained on the market for the 1972 harvest. Its first season was the 1969 harvest, using many features form the former models such as two fan cleaning system, three speed gear box and drum position. This was a large combine, having longer straw walkers, heavy duty open-grate concaves, and larger 103hp Perkins 6.354 diesel engine. The 5000 was replaced by the Italian Laverda combines sold under Bamfords name.

The Parent company began to struggle in the 1980's in a climate of rapid economic change. Amid financial struggles, it was forced to sell its farm equipment division to KHD (Klockner-Humboldt-Deutz) AG of Germany in 1985, the owners of Deutz-Fahr, which was renamed Deutz-Allis. Deutz-Allis was later sold and became what is now the AGCO corporation (AGCO). The company closed its offices in Milwaukee in 1999.

Jones Cruiser

David Jones opened a manufacturing facility known as Esmor Works, based at an old lead processing site at Rhosesmor, Mold in North Wales, where he produced a static baler followed by a pick up PTO driven baler. The introduction of their self propelled combine, the Jones Pilot in 1957 proved a disaster for the company. It was powered by a David Brown vaporising engine. An improved model, the Cruiser which had a Fordson Major engine and a 7ft cut was launched the following year, but few were sold. The combine had a low level operator position which was unpopular, the machines were all recalled and scrapped, and the company concentrated on balers. The Crusier was marketed by Bamfords alongside Allis Chalmers models, Eventually Jones was taken over by Allis- Chalmers.

DAVID BROWN

In 1955 David Brown bought Harris, McGregor and Guest Ltd which were based at Leigh Lancahshire. They made Albion farm machines and 67,000 Albion binders A David Brown trailer combine was made at Leigh which use d a Swedish design built under licence. It had a 5½ft cut and weighed 1½ tons.

LANZ

In 1955, the Lanz MD260S self propelled tanker model combine completed its first harvest. It was a straight through machine and was on display at a show that year. Eleven machines were supplied for the 1955 harvest by the sole suppliers H. Leverton and Co of Spalding and another fifty were imported from Germany the following year. They were powered by a Perkins L4 diesel engine and a tanker version cost £2,258 with an 8ft 6in header. A feature was the hydraulic adjustment of the pick- up reel.

VIKING/AVA- AB BOLINDER-MUNKTELL

Marketed by Viking Farm Machinery Ltd of Ivybridge Devon and manufactured by AB Bolinder-Munktell. of Eskilstuna Swedon, whose combines were known as AVA. The Swedish firm, ARVIKA-Thermaenius had a reputation for producing quality high output machines. They began when John Thermaenius built threshing machines in the 1860's. The factory moved to Hallsberg and the company merged with AVA which was founded in 1885. They made mowers and binders under the Viking and Hercules names.

Viking went on to become BM Volvo distributed by Bamfords of Uttoxeter, when the company was taken over by the Volvo Group the Viking name was dropped.

Johan Theo fron Munktell founded Munktells business which produced the first Swedish steam engines for railway use and later threshing machines followed. They merged with Bolinders of Stockholm following the depression in the 1930's.

In 1950, Bolinder Munktell launched their first self propelled combine, the 9ft MST 91. Two other manufacturers, Thermaenius in 1946 and Westrasmaskiner (Activ) in 1948 started production.

In 1960, BM bought Arvika Thermaenius, the AVA farm machinery conglomerate who made the Theermaenius combines in Hallsberg. AVA exported to England. The merger resulted in a concentration of all combine production in Hallsberg. The BT45 and ST 256 had been produced in Arvika and BM combines were made in Flen.

In 1940, BM designed their first combine, a 5ft trailed machine driven from the tractors pto known as 'Belles-Moore'.

In 1950, the BM Company was sold with profit to Volvo and BM combine production was moved from Eskilstuna to Flen. By 1969, BM took over the responsibility for selling the Aktiv combines. The whole company name was changed to Volvo BM in March 1973. In 1977, the farm division of Volvo BM developed Self Propelled combines in co operation with Aktiv Fisher AB in Morgongava. In 1980, Volvo left the scene after more than 120 years of making threshing machines, selling out to the new owner of Aktiv.

Two new models were launched, the Volvo BM/Aktiv 1110 and 1130 which were direct followers of the S 800 and S 830.

Munktell combines were originally silver with orange lettering. The Thermaenius combines were also silver but with black lettering, the Aktiv combines were green. From around 1955 the BM combines changed to the blue grey, which lasted until the 1960's when it changed to green.

Viking Farm Machinery Ltd was a subsidiary formed by the agricultural engineering firm Watkins and Rhoseveare Tractors Ltd, whose base was Ivybridge in Devon, and later had branches in Cornwall and Okehampton in Devon. Aside from exporting Fordson tractors, they branched out into other machinery, and under the name Watveare Overseas Ltd, imported machinery to Britain. Another branch called Western Machinery and Equipment Company Plymouth brought in the first AVA ST67 combine to the UK. A sales leaflet of the period states the combine had a large diameter drum with six beater bars 52hp Ford engine and 55 bushel grain tank and was imported by Farm Machinery and Accessories Ltd of Ahsburton Devon.

Viking had made the 7ft cut ST67 from 1953, which was a three wheel machine. They were straight through models in bagger or tanker versions and were fitted with a single shaker shoe instead of straw walkers. In 1957, the Devon importers advertised the self propelled 7ft cut ST67 as a high quality machine for English conditions - it was available as a tanker or bagger for £2,100. In Britain, they had a four cylinder Ford 592 E diesel engine, and it had a hydraulic pick up reel. These were the first Swedish built harvesters to come to the UK. There were problems due to the engine being mounted between the driving wheels, and posing a fire risk, and instability due to the three wheels. The ST 68 available as a tanker and bagger model with 8ft cut was launched at the Royal Show in 1958 by Viking Farm Machinery of Ivybridge, who shared the same premises at Ivybridge as Western Machinery. This model had a choice of grain tank or bagging platform, 8ft 5in cut, 55 bushel grain tank and 52hp Ford diesel engine. The Viking models were increased with a smaller 6ft cut ST256 and larger ST610/612, with Perkins diesel engines. In Power Farming Magazine in 1957, it was reported that a farmer from Arundel Sussex had the first of the new ST612 Viking combines from Sweden after having seeing the machine at the Royal Show. It had a 12ft cutter bar and a 71in wide drum.

The ST256 and its successor the 7ft cut ST257 were quite popular with 10,000 built until 1967, although AVA played only a small part in the development of combine harvesters during the 1950's and 1960's

VOLVO

Volvo BM bought the Ava-Thermaenius company in 1960 as a result of a division of Volvo called Bolinder-Munktell Eskilstuna in Sweden deciding to become a farm machinery manufacturer, offering a full range of farm equipment. The three straw walker Ava ST257 was still produced and imported to the UK, with many being sold from the Kings Lynn branch. This was available as a tanker or bagger combine, the reel and 7ft or 8ft cut table were hydraulically controlled, and had a 22in diameter drum and Perkins C4/99 4 cylinder 35hp diesel engine and 39 bushel grain tank. It was an easy to operate small combine for use in both small and large fields. The larger straight through S 1000 A had a 6 cylinder 80hp Volvo-Penta diesel engine, four straw walkers, and was available with 10 or 12ft cutting widths, and grain tank capacity of 55 bushels with optional bagging off equipment.

Viking Farm Machinery also became importers of the Volvo BM combines. After a deal was made with Viking, these were marketed by Bamfords of Uttoxeter until the 1970's but the designs of the original Ava had gone. Bamfords had lost their agency for Claeys after the Belgian company was acquired by New Holland. Under Bamfords, sales of the Volvo BM combines increased, especially for the smaller ST257, as well as harvesters originally made by BM, the S1000 and S1000 A models. The three straw walker S830 from Bolinder-Munktell was described as a light weight machine with a high capacity, it had a 44 bushel grain tank, 9ft cutting width, Perkins 4.154 56hp engine and an optional bagging off attachment. The larger four straw walker S950 with 66 bushel grain tank came in 10ft, 12ft and 14ft cutting widths, and had a powerful Volvo D50 6 cylinder 117hp engine and large 2ft diameter drum providing a fly wheel effect with high inertia giving a high output. By 1971 Volvo imports ended when Bamfords entered into Allis-Chalmers machinery, including the Allis 5000.

AKTIV

The 5½ft cut was a PTO straight through machine, the Model M which was on the market for some years and was available as a tanker or bagger. It was imported from Sweden by Western Machinery of Ivybridge Devon. The machine had a tank capacity of 33 bushels, 4ft wide drum and the bagging platform could carry 10cwt of grain. This was one of the last trailed combines on the British market and regarded by many farmers as the best trailed combine available.

The Aktiv 800/1000 where self propelled combines sold through Burgess, and marketed by Western Machinery and Equipment.

The three straw walker Aktiv 800 model had a 7ft 3in cutting width, and was powered by a Perkins 42hp diesel engine, with 40 bushel grain tank capacity. The larger four walker 1000 model had a 9ft 3in cutting width and was powered by a 60hp Perkins diesel engine and had a grain tank capacity of 48 bushels. Drum diameter on birth models was just under 18in.

Most trailed machines had disappeared from British farms by the late 1950's but the Allis All-Crop 60, International B-64 and Aktiv Model M were still to be seen.

JF

In 1961 JF Farm Machines of Denmark re introduced the idea of building a combine around the tractor, which was first tried by Claas thirty years earlier, the combine was sold by JF Farm Machines of Gloucester.

JF Fabriken was Denmark's largest producer and exporter of farm machinery, mainly grassland tackle such as mowers and forage harvesters, with factories and associated companies in the UK, Western Germany, Belgium and Spain.

The first JF side mounted combine, the bagger model MS 5 was first marketed in the early 60's to replace the binder, and offered an alternative to the self propelled combine, by letting the tractor form the power unit, the cost of the machine was kept low. The tractor was reversed into the side mounted combine and connecting could be undertaken by one man in a few minutes. The combine as connected to the drawbar of the tractor, and it had an outstanding manoeuvrability. Both types could be adapted for use as bagging models. It had a 5ft cut, 27in wide drum, and was said to have a good driving quality on hillsides due to it slow centre of gravity and by transference of weight to the tractor and in good conditions was said to have a capacity of 30cwt an hour. In 1967, the first JF tanker model, with 6ft was introduced, to meet the demand for a larger machine.

The 8ft cut JF MS 90 "Grainflash" with full hydraulic control, incorporating hydraulic controls to the reel and cutting platform. The MS 90 sales leaflet states that it could be fitted to a tractor in less than five minutes. The 6ft model needed a 40hp tractor and the 10ft model required a 50hp tractor, the combine cost £5,000 in 1976. It was available in tanker or bagger models.

Later came the Carri-Combine MS910 This was a tractor mounted requiring 60hp from the tractor pto, it had a 3m cutter bar, 850mm drum width, 450mm drum diameter, four straw walkers, tank capacity of 1630 litres, and optional straw chopper and performance monitor. List price in 1985 was £9,750.

There was also a smaller JF 707, which had a 7ft cutting width, 1290 litre grain tank and capacity of 4 ton an hour, requiring a power requirement of 48hp at the pto.

The Carri-Combine MS910E required 60hp tractor, pto driven, it had a 3m header, drum size 850mm wide and 450mm diameter, four straw walkers, grain tank capacity of 1630 litres and options of a straw chopper and performance monitor. List price in 1985 was £11,000.

These combines were exported to 45 countries.

KIDD

Kidds' Trailed stripper combine was on show at the 1990 Smithfield Show, and was aimed at the smaller farmer who could not afford a new self propelled machine and did not want to buy second hand, and also the larger grower who had several combines and who wished to reduce capital investment in machinery. It was originally developed at the Silsoe Research Institute, formerly AFRC Engineering. and taken on in 1990 by Kidd of Devizes. This was a tractor drawn machine, requiring a 100hp tractor, it was put on trial at AFRC Engineering in Bedfordshire and much of the trial work was undertaken in Tayside, Scotland in 1990, and monitored by Kidds' engineers. One prototype which had the mustard and brown livery of AFRC, was on trial the following year, with an aim to market it in 1992. It had a Shelbourne Reynolds stripper header at the front, behind it was a self-mechanism not very different to a conventional combine, but the layout broke new ground. The whole machine was fully offset behind the tractor at the end of a long drawbar. With the stripper header, hardly any straw came through the combine, but one of the problems with using the stripper header was the standing straw left behind it. Output from the 10ft stripper header was 17 tonne an hour, it had a 4 tonne grain tank and estimated price as £40,000. Many people wanted to buy the combine, it did work, although only the chassis, tank and rotary separators were made at Kidd, the other parts, namely elevators, augers and internal components were off the shelf parts from a New Holland 8050. However plans to produce a few hundred in 1993 did not materialise, due to Kidd being sold to the Danish firm Taarup early in 1991, who did not wish to continue with the project. The one prototype was returned to Silsoe.

LAVERDA

In 1873, Pietro Laverda established "Ditta Pietro Laverda", the first craftsman's workshop that produced farming implements, wine making machines and bell-tower clocks in S Giorgia di Perlena in Provence of Vicenza in Italy. The Company then moved to Breganze, which was to remain the headquarters for more than seventy years. With mechanization beginning they made threshing machines, straw cutters, grain fans, wine presses and corn shellers. In 1919, after the end of the First World War activities were resumed with the help of Pietro Laverda's sons, Giovanni and Antonio. They patented new models including a hydraulic press. In 1930, the two grandsons of the founder took over the company and Laverda made the first mowing machine. In 1938, they introduced the first reaper-binder, the ML6 the forerunner of a series of machines that was to influence Italian grain cultivation for decades, this was the beginning of Laverda's involvement with harvesting machines. In 1956, they produced the first Italian self-propelled combine harvester, the M60 model. By 1963, they had introduced the M120 combine. In 1971 Laverda launched the M100AL, the first combine with a cross wise and longitudinal self-levelling system. Available through importers, Bamfords Ltd of Uttoxeter, the M150, M120, M110 and M84 were available for the 1976 season. Their new combine range the M92, M112, M132 and M152 were launched in the 1970's Laverda built a new plant in Breganze and began a partnership with Fiat. They brought out new models the 3000 series in 1983, with the 3850 being unveiled in 1984. In 1984 Fiatagri launched the 3550, a four walker combine with a new 6 cylinder 130hp Fiat engine for the following harvest. With header width choices of 3.1m, 3.6m and 4.2m, this superseded the 3450 model, and a higher output 3890 based on the 3850, replaces the 3900 model at the top of the range. This had a 200hp Fiat engine and new hydrostatic transmission and header widths of 4.8m, 5.4m and 6m. Based at Bury St Edmunds, Fiatagri UK Ltd marketed the 3400 to 3750, 3790, 3850 and 3890 straw walkers models in 1989, and MX240 and MX300 rotary models. Prices in 1989 ranged from £41,820 for the 75hp 3400 model to £82,065 for the largest 148hp 3890 walker model.

The "levelling system" was developed for combines in 1992, and the MCS-Multi Crop separator system for separating the product. The Breganze plant was taken over by Argo SpA, the Company belonging to the Morra family, owners of the Landini Company. In 2002/2003 Laverda introduced the LXE series, M series and the new Self Levelling Combine Series. The REV series was launched for the 2005-2006 sales year. The following year, the new LCS Laverda crop System was launched. Since 2004, Laverda had been working with AGCO supplying them with its combines in the MF, Fendt and Challenger livery. In 2007, Argo Spa officially announced the establishment of a 50% joint venture between Laverda SpA and AGCO Corporation, based in Duluth Georgia, which was a large distributor of agricultural equipment worldwide.

FORTSCHRITT

Kombinat Fortschritt Landmaschinen of East Germany began making combines in 1948, and in 1989 had an annual production of about 5,500 machines. This is an East German brand of combines and other agricultural machinery, made by VEB Fortschritt. These combines were imported into the UK by Bonhill Engineering Co of Thetford Norfolk. The company became MDW which was taken over by Case IH in 1977.

A Fortschritt E175 made in 1965 was one of the first self propelled models with a 4 cylinder diesel motor EM 4-15-5, was a straight through combine and capable of harvesting 4 ton of wheat an hour.

Introduced at the Royal Show in 1974, the Forschritt E512 had been at work that harvest in Ingham Bury St Edmunds. A 14ft model cost £8,500 and £300 for an optional cab.

An E512 combine was priced at £16,800 in 1978. Grain loss monitors, automatic height control, maize header and a 19ft grain header were also optional. The E512 had a 4VD Diesel engine and four straw walkers with header width of 5.70m and 4.20m and had a drum of 1,278mm width and 600mm diameter and a rated throughput of 15-20 metric ton an hour. In 1985, the E516 was given a redesigned cab made by Richford Farm Machinery Sales Ltd which offered better operator comfort with tinted glass all round, and in cab cooling. The E516 had header width of 7.60m wide, 8 VD engine OF 228hp, five straw walkers, and hydrostatic transmission, and capacity of up to 2.56 hectares an hour.

The E524 had more electronics, with a control panel which monitored all engine functions, and sieves, straw walkers, augers and elevators and shaft speeds, and had automatically controlled table height and fore and aft flotation controlled by springs whose tension was controlled automatically as the table was raised and lowered, and also had an auger reverser on the header.

LELY VICTORY
FISHER HUMPHRIES

These did not conform to the standard combines made in the 1960's.

Fisher Humphries Ltd was based at Crudwell, Malmesbury, Wiltshire. Lely was the successor to Fisher Humphries, the former threshing machine manufacturer, and was based at Wootten Bassett, Wiltshire.

Originally manufactured under licence in Crudwell, the Fisher Humphries combine was a product resulting from a tie with the European Dechntreiter Company. Early combines were plagued with problems, Lely purchased Fisher Humphries in the mid 1960's and production then moved to Wootton Bassett, when they launched the MK II design. The folding header was retained, in 14ft or 18ft cut, and there were improvements to machine design and the Victory was claimed to be the world's largest combine at the time.

The Victory combine was built from 1965 to 1980 with a production run of around 300 units mainly used in the UK and Europe.

Fisher Humphries also made and sold the JD 240S and JD 210S self propelled tanker combines independently of Lely in 1966, with standard header of 7ft and 8ft 6in. Both tanker models, the 210S had a 52hp Perkins diesel engine, three straw walkers and the 240S had a Perkins 58hp engine. Capacity was said to be between 6 tons and 7 tons an hour according to model.

The self propelled Fisher-Humphries Victory Combine, a Lely invention, on the market in 1964 had a 14ft cut, and was capable of passing through normal gateways without removing the table. The change was achieved hydraulically in a few seconds. It was powered by a 105hp Perkins diesel engine wand had a 70 bushel grain tank.

The larger Lely Victory model had a folding header of 4.2 or 5.4m wide. Lely was a pioneer of hydrostatic transmission. The British built Lely Victory Mark II and Mark III, which were later models, were the only models in the world at one time in the 1960's with folding headers, where two hydraulic rams were used to fold the two sections up vertically to less than 10ft for travelling on the road. At the Royal Show in 1969 they had a RASE Silver Award for this innovation. They also won awards from the Scottish Agricultural Association. To activate the folding header, all that was needed was to push a lever, the table would hydraulically unfold, after inserting a locking pin, the combine was ready for work. They featured advanced hydrostatic steering and hydraulic controls, reel speed was hydraulically adjustable as was the up and down fore and aft. Other innovations were micro switches being fitted for the straw walkers and grain elevator drives, giving warning to the driver of any blockages. They were a high capacity machine with grain tank of 100 bushels. With a transport width of 9ft 6in and an output of up to 17 tons an hour, they had five straw walkers and a large 23.5in diameter drum. They also had the option of hydrostatic or manual transmission, hydrostatic was standard on the larger model, they had a 14ft or 18ft header, which folded, each half being driven by its own hydraulic motor which was interconnected with the other for identical speed balance, with speed being adjustable from the platform. The reel fore and aft and up and down was hydraulically controlled. The power came from a Ford 2715E 6 cylinder 108hp diesel engine with optional Ford 135hp type 270ET turbo charged engine and an option of the Victory cab. In 1980, the Mark II was priced at £23,253 with 18ft cut table and the Mark III with 18ft cut table £27,888. The cab complete with air filtration fan and electric wiper was £1,071, plus £1,092 for the larger engine. The earlier MK II was also sold with a Perkins 6.354 Diesel engine giving 105hp, with optional Turbo version, the T6.354 giving 135hp. It had a ZF gearbox, 4 forward and 1 reverse gearbox with a traction variator fitted. Later MK II models were modified with the power unit changing to Ford, a N/A 2715E engine, of 105hp or optional Turbocharged 2507ET engine of 135hp. The shaker shoe in later MK II models was changed, and larger grain tank fitted. Colour scheme changed from the all blue with red wheels to white and blue.

Cabs were optional, made by Cabcraft and fitted with Air conditioning blower unit.

The MK III which joined the MK II later had an identical threshing mechanism, but the Traction variator was replaced by the Linde Hydrostatic Unit, one of the first hydrostatic combines available at the time.

BIZON

All Polish combine harvesters were made at one factory which according to machinery journals at the time produced 2,900 in 1974, with a target of 10,000 by 1980. In 1974, the two models made were the Bizon and Bizon Super. The Bizon Super had a 105hp engine and drum size of 49in wide and 23in diameter, and was built at the FMZ factory in Flock near Warsaw. A Bizon Gigant, a larger version of the same design was at the time of mid 1974 planned for production by 1975. This had been on trial in 1973, and had headers up to 26ft and a 220hp engine with hydrostatic transmission. This was a high capacity combine with 62in wide and 23in diameter drum, with hydraulic adjustable reel positions and air conditioned cab. The electronic system which monitors the total mass of crop entering the feed elevator was a new feature and was quite advanced. The combine automatically adjusted the travel speed, reel and intake elevator according to the mass of crop.

The Polish Bizon combines were brought into the UK through Agromet-Motoimport who also imported Ursus tractors. The British branch was known as Ursus Bizon (GB) Ltd based at Nedham Market in Suffolk. Combine production began in 1954, and the company was producing 6000 machines annually. Bizon was taken over by CNH in 1998.

GLORIA

Traynor Motors of Dublin handled the Romanian Gloria combine and Universal tractors. A 10ft cut Gloria C12 cost £9,995 in 1975. These machines were also available in 12ft or 14ft cuts and were powered by a Perkins 6.345 diesel 118hp engine. They were an identical specification to the 120 Laverda.

EPPLE-MOBIL

Made in Austria by Epple-Buxbaum-Werke of Wels, the machine was available in the 1960's and was aimed at medium to larger size farms. The Epple Mobil 1000 had a four cylinder 75hp Perkins engine, four walkers and a twin threshing system with two cylinders and two concaves, and a 57 bushel grain tank and was supplied with a 10ft header. The Epple Mobil 211 had a 7ft cut, 4 cylinder 41hp Perkins diesel engine, and the 250 model had a 8ft cut, 4 cylinder Perkins 52hp engine, three straw walkers and 28 bushel grain tank with option of bagging platform. Sole importers were Eurotrac Imports Ltd of Thames Street, Staines in Essex.

DECHENTREITER COMBINE

There were some models of combine which made their way to Britain, but did not last. This model was available in the UK for the 1952 harvest, after being introduced at the Smithfield Show in 1951. Made in Germany, it was imported by STA-Sale Tilney Agricultural Ltd of Wokingham Berkshire and was a straight through machine from the cutter bar to the drum and the built in trusser on the back of the combine, fitted with a 4 cylinder air cooled engine of around 24hp. A tractor pulled model, it was built up on a main frame of tubular welded steel. It had a bagging platform, and chaff could be either bagged up from the operators platform or blown from a spout. Operational width was 69in at the cutter bar to 55in at the drum and 47in in the bale chamber. Controls for header height and vertical and horizontal reel control were within reach of the operators platform, which was said to be a complete one man control unit from the from the bagging platform.

BLANCH

Manufactured by Leon Clays of Zedelgem Belgium, these models were made for A B Blanch and Co Ltd of Crudwell Wiltshire, and were priced at £1,995. They were 5 walker machines, with a Perkins L4 diesel engine and came as tanker or bagger versions with 10 and 14ft cut.

KOLA

Described as a Hydromat High Capacity Combine, with 10, 15 and 20ft cutting widths, 6 cylinder 108hp diesel engine, and 4 straw walkers, 80 bushel grain tank, this model came from Germany and was said to be the first production model high capacity combine in the world with hydrostatic transmission, and was said to have a capacity of up to 14 tons an hour.

DEUTZ-FAHR

Deutz originated in Germany, its history can be traced back to its founders August Otto and Eugene Langen in 1894, who were the inventors of the first four stroke spark-ignition engine. They launched into tractors after World War I when there was a labour shortage. Deutz converted water-cooled engines into air-cooled ones for better dependability for military equipment during the Second World War. The air-cooled engine was still a hallmark of Deutz until the 1990's.

The Deutz threshing machine section was founded in 1870 by Michael Kodel in Lauingen on the Danube as a mechanical workshop, the company started making threshing machines in 1890. Fifty years later saw development in combine harvesters and in 1966, the first Hydromat rolled off the production line.

Deutz merged with Fahr in 1961 to become Deutz-Fahr.

KHD, (Klockner-Humboldt-Deutz), became the owner of Deutz-Fahr. In 1969, the Company joined the KHD Group and then became an independent member of KHD Holding, trading under the name of Deutz Fahr Emtesysteme GmbH. In 1977, Fahr was taken over as a branch of KHD, and development began on a new combine, the MD80. By 1981, full line production began under the joint name of Deutz Fahr.

In the early 1980's, the Deutz-Fahr Company had a surplus of cash and purchased the American Allis-Chalmers Company. That venture turned out to be a financial disaster and Deutz-Allis was sold to AGCO in 1988.

After retreating to its established customer base in its German homeland, the Deutz-Fahr Company never recovered, and in 1995 it had to be sold.

FAHR

Fahr was another West German company making combines, based at Gottmadingen. The company also made foragers, tedders and other machinery. It was founded in the 1870's by Johann George Fahr.

A Fahr MD 1 self propelled combine was shown at the German Agricultural Engineering Show at Hamburg in 1951, a bagger type with a 7ft 6in cutter bar and powered by a 25hp diesel engine. The drum was about 1ft 2in in diameter and it had a revolving corkscrew type of divider common on German binders. From this evolved the MDL which was made in 1961. Fahr was taken over by KHD in 1968 to create Koln Deutz Fahr. Fahr of Gottmadingen and took over the plant at Lauingen in 1970, formerly owned by Kodel, for a second combine plant. By 1977, Fahr was taken over as a branch of KHD and development started on the MD80.

Deutz Fahr's most powerful combine to date is the companies first rotary, the 7545 which is 450hp and the 350hp 7535. An agreement was reached with Vassalli Fabril of Argentina. Combines will initially be supplied direct from Argentina, but SDF will build the rotary machines at its combine plant in Croatia.

COMBI

Tested in 1958 and marketed in 1959, the Kola Combi was a self propelled combine with a bagging platform and was made in Germany by Kodel and Bohm, and distributed by Machinery Distributers Ltd of Lucan in Co Dublin. It had a 34hp Mercedes diesel engine, 6ft 3in and 6ft 9in cutter bar options and was said to have a capacity of one and a half to two tons an hour. A later model in 1962, the Favourite with option of a bagging platform or tanker model, had a 8ft 4in cut, Fordson 55hp diesel engine, three straw walkers and straw trusser attached.

ORSI

The Super 800 Harvester-Thresher was made by Orsi Pietro and Figlio S.p.A Tortona, in Italy this self propelled model with bagging off platform had a 4 cylinder 50hp engine.

UNIVERSAL

A few of these came to UK they were made by Zmaj, Zemun, Industrija Poljoprivrednih Masina, and had four walkers, 10ft and 12ft headers, and IMR/036/TA 78hp diesel engine.

VETY

Made in Denmark by Vestjden, these were 5 and 6ft trailed combines, and operated by means of a fully hydraulic system independent of the tractor, and came as a bagger or tanker model.

Scrap

During 208, the strong demand for scrap metal has seen prices rise to between £190 and £240 per tonne in many parts of the country, over double what they were the previous year. A depot of a large recycling group, EMR at Tyneside said scrap prices were in the region £275 a tonne at one time. Another scrap dealer in Lincolnshire expected strong scrap prices to continue for the foreseeable future. This has had a knock on effect on the future of older combines, with some breakers clearing their yards for scrap, so reducing available spare parts, and farmers were prompted to clear their yards of older redundant machinery for scrap rather than retaining them for parts and it has meant that many classic machines that could have had potential for restoration have been sent to the scrap yards.

PDI Checks

Undertaken pre delivery of all new combines to the farm, involves:
Check engine oil level
Coolant level
Air filter seating and air filter cartridge
Check on rotary screen and drive belt and tension it up
Check for transport damage - guards, chassis, wheel rims etc
Remove any transport clamps for the cab roof, and securing wires from unloading auger and guards, steps etc
Remove components from inside of grain tank stored for transport
Mirrors and accessories, fire extinguishers, radio aerial fitted
Tracking is checked
Pivoting steering axle, remove stop bolts
Rear axle changed from transport to working position
Oil levels in gearboxes,
main gearbox behind front drive shaft

reduction gear boxes where wheels bolted to two gear boxes for the rotors
Transfer gear box on the engine

Oil levels on the header
1 rape knife drive on left of header at the back
2 wobble box oil level

Auger extension plates in centre, which narrows the space for the intake of crop to feeder housing, removed

Transmission wheels brakes
1 Nuts and bolts etc checked
2 Brake fluid level

Engine
1 Coolant levels and condition
2 Air intake pipe, checked tightened if necessary
3 Fuel in tank, enough in it

Gearboxes/Drive/Hydraulics/Electrics
Hydraulic system and engine coolant checked for leaks
Battery charge level checked

Auto Contour working
Concave settings set as for factory setting from which any adjustments are taken

Grain tank Sensors and warning beacon outside cab-check working, these show when tank is half and three quarters and full on Cebis display)
Main Bearings greased

Grain Strippers

Dating back to the 1840s, the stripper harvester is an Australian invention. The Sunshine stripper was invented in 1845, and sold in considerable numbers by the H V McKay company. This company became associated with Massey Harris in Australia in the 1930's and products sold included the Sunshine self binders. In the late 1940's, a Wild Harvest Thresher was introduced from Australia, which had an engine driven stripper rotor. and two cylinders to separate the grain from the chaff, The grain was bagged off and the chaff returned to the ground.

Further development work on the stripper took place in Britain during the mid 1980's, with an Institute of Engineering Research prototype machine, Shelbourne Reynolds Engineering produced several grain strippers for the 1988 harvest. The quick attach SRE stripper header replaced the conventional combine cutter bar and is suitable for harvesting wheat, barley, linseed peas and oil seed rape. The stripper rotor had eight rows of key hole shaped teeth runnin gin an anti clockwise direction, which removes the ears and loose leaves from the standing crop, which are carried to the combine threshing cylinder by an auger and elevator. Both these and the earlier harvesters left the straw standing for chopping or ploughing in. Kidds Farm Machinery exhibited a trailed stripper harvester at the 1990 Smithfield Show. This had a Shelbourne Reynolds stripper header drum and concave, sieves and fan with rotary separators instead of straw walkers.

Cabs

Many drivers had to wait until 1974 before cabs were provided and then they were only provided with the more expensive models. By the late 1970's, a good quality cab was standard on most new combines of all makes.

Part

1

CLAAS

HUCKEPACK

First produced in 1956, and displayed at the German DLG exhibition in Hannover that year, it had a 800mm drum width and cutter bar width of 2.10m. It was a three straw walker machine with a bagging platform. This was a self propelled machine for the smaller farmer which could be modified into an implement carrier at other times of the year. The prime mover used a 12hp diesel engine and the combine unit used a VW industrial 34hp engine. The idea of fitting a combine onto a prime mover did not catch on and it was discontinued in 1960. A sales brochure appeared in English, but it is not known how many were used in Britain.

NOTE
Technical specifications and options for individual models are taken from manufacturers sales brochures and change on an annual basis.

COLUMBUS

First year of production 1958

The Columbus, together with the Europa, followed from the earlier SF and was designed for smaller farms.

— **Bottom Right**

This one spent all its working life near Forden, Welshpool in Wales, before being stored in a shed on the Plowdon Estate, Shropshire. When the storage space was lost, it was sold to David Rawlings of Greete near Ludlow in Shropshire, who takes it to the annual Brimfield Vintage Club Working Event. It had an output of about 5 to 6 acres a day. It had a 6ft cutter bar, with hydraulic height control, and was offered with a choice of either a 29hp or 38hp VW industrial engine or 4 cylinder Perkins diesel engine. It was a three straw walker combine, offered as a bagger or with a grain tank, which had a capacity of 30 bushels. Some were fitted with a straw trusser. A 6ft tanker model would have cost £1,570. 10s in 1963.

— **Above** A Huckepack in the German Museum, The DLM near Stuttgart.

CLAAS SF

SF was an abbreviation for self propelled in German - Selbstfahrer. First introduced in 1953, it was produced for ten years. It was originally known as the Hercules, but later the name was changed to SF in 1955. It was offered with 2.40m, 3m and 3.60m cutter bar widths, as a tanker or bagger model with choice of 60hp 6 cylinder diesel or 56hp 4 cylinder petrol engine. According to a sales brochure of the period, a contractor wrote that 70 cwt per hour could be harvested in standing wheat, it was considered to be a high output machine at the time, with 4 tonnes an hour output. The SF was introduced at the Royal Show held in Blackpool priced at £2,300.

— RIGHT

An SF in storage in the Combine World building at Saxham Bury St Edmunds.

— **RIGHT**

CLAAS SF at Morris Corfield, Broseley, Shropshire. This combine has been in the area all its life. It was the first self propelled combine sold at Morris Corfield of Much Wenlock, to Milner Whiteman of Arscott farm, Posenhall, Shropshire. George Pugh, salesman at the time sold this to Forresters of Willey Farm, Benthall, in 1963 for the 1964 season. The SF was then sold to Jo Rowson, Cleobury North. George Green of Cleobury North, Jo Rowson's son in law, bought this SF for £200 in 1969, when his father-in-law had a farm sale. George Green had been driving this combine. Just after the purchase, two people appeared asking if George would continue to do their combining for them, so the SF carried on cutting about 200 acres until it was replaced by a Senator, which was also bought at a sale. The SF then came to the dealers yard at Benthall, as it was one of the first John Corfield, one of the founders, sold.

— **RIGHT**

The CLAAS SF next to a Lexion 570+ Montana.

STANDARD MATADOR

Bought for preservation and restoration, in my own collection

Purchased for £250 from a lady farmer near Claxton in Yorkshire in 2006, to save it from the scrap merchant, this B registered Matador Standard still worked cutting a few acres of barley, until a local contractor was called in to make harvest a quicker job, a year or two before its sale. The model pictured is a four straw walker combine with a 10ft header, and Perkins 4 cylinder 68hp engine. Models were also available with options of 8ft 6in and 12ft cutter bars. Drum size was 18in diameter

and 49in wide. The grain tank held 47 bushels or 26 cwt of wheat. The price of a Standard Matador new in 1963 would have been in the region of £2,300 according to cutter bar size, and £2,800 for the Giant model. It was claimed to have delivered 6 tons per hour, but in a good season quoted in 1962, it could match the larger Matador Giant's output of 8 tons per hour.

In November 1962, the 10ft tanker model cost £2,286. 10s , with £60 extra for power steering and £175 for a straw press.

First produced in 1962, to replace the SF to meet a growing demand for larger machines, it was by contemporary standards at the time a large combine. The Standard version followed after the larger Matador Gigant or Giant, introduced in 1961. Cutter bars became larger, and the grain tank now became standard rather than an option, although straw presses and bagging off platforms were still available on the Matadors and Servo Steering (hydraulically assisted Steering) was offered in the sales brochure.

MERCURY

The 'Mercury' also known as a Mecur was launched in 1963, to fill a gap between the larger four straw walker Matador Standard and smaller three straw walker Europa and Columbus models. The sales slogan applied to it is 4 tons plus for less than £2.000 in November 1962. When tested by the N.I.A.E. its average overall throughput in wheat was 4½ tons per hour.

— BELOW

The author's Claas Mercury is seen at a recent Leominster Vintage Club working day.

This Mercury has a 8ft 6in header and is powered by a Perkins 4 cylinder 52hp engine which is offset to the right of the driver's platform. It is in the collection belonging to Kevin Norris of Alveley, Bridgnorth in Shropshire.

It was a four straw walker combine, with the drum being 18in diameter and 42in wide. A new disowning system extended the concave by 3 bars when engaged. It was offered with cutting widths of 8½ft or 10ft and was extremely up to date by contemporary standards, having special features of hydraulic cutter bar and reel control and the drive variator was also hydraulically controlled. Grain lifters and dividers were offered as standard with the combine, and an option was a straw chopper or straw press with two knotters. The grain tank held 47 bushels or 26 cwt of wheat. There was an option of a bagging off platform, although most models were now the tanker version. Hydraulically assisted steering was also offered as an option.

Costing in the region of £2000 when first imported, one of the first which was imported to the UK went to Morris Corfield in Shropshire. In 1963, the list price for a tanker Mercury with 10ft header was £2,060. As in the Europa, the engine is positioned over the offside wheel and the grain tank holds 47 bushels.

SENATOR 70

The Senator was launched in 1966 to replace the Matador, with a totally new design, with large side panels. The Mercator which was introduced after the Senator was marketed for a short time in Britain, but was not so popular in Britain and was phased out, the Senator remained in the UK. Senators were the first combines in the CLAAS leaf green, apart from a few late Matadors, and they also featured the redesigned CLAAS logo. The first Senator had cutters bars of 14 to 20ft with 10ft and 12ft options, and had a 105hp engine, and 88 bushel grain tank, and weighed 6 tons. During this time, numbers were added to model names to distinguish differences in size within the same family, the Senator 60, 70, 80 and 85 followed, replacing the first standard Senator and Protector models. The Senator 70 had a standard 10ft cutter bar with options of 12ft and 14ft, and grain tank capacity of 2500 litres. With a 6 cylinder 105hp engine, Senators had the option of Mercedes or Perkins. The standard CLAAS 18in diameter drum was retained, and all Senators had hydrostatic steering.

— **OPPOSITE PAGE**

The model shown here is from my own collection and dates from 1975. It has a Cab Craft cab. By now, cabs and straw choppers were offered as options, cabs appeared as an option for the first time in the price list in 1967 for Senator. The first cabs were not designed to reduce the drivers exposure to dust. Often they were too hot inside with no ventilation.

This Senator 70 still cuts about 25 acres annually at Clyro near Hay-on-Wye on the Welsh borders. Hydraulic unloading augers were still not available on many combines, on this one it is manually swung into place.

Senator 70 and the name of the importer, Manns of Saxham, appears on the straw walker hood.

SENATOR 85

The largest of the Senator range, this 4 straw walker model still cuts about 20 acres annually.

— **BELOW**

Adam Nicholls cuts about twenty acres in the Abberley district of Worcestershire using a Senator 85 with 10ft header, in small fields which are inaccessible to the large modern contractors combine, which cuts the bulk of the harvest on his farm. This combine has a manually operated unloading auger, the grain unloading auger was hydraulically adjusted on this model from 1978. It was offered with a 14ft header as standard with options of 10ft and 12ft.

As cutter bars became larger, the header came with a quick lock as standard, to enable Quick detachment. The CLAAS ISS Intensive Separation System, featured on later 85 models. This was a shaker agitator and rake times mounted on two crank shafts and a larger 6 cylinder 115hp diesel engine with the option of being water or air cooled. Options listed in a sales brochure of the period include operators cab, straw chopper and 3 and 4 row maize picker. A Senator 85 with standard 14ft header was priced at £17,275 in November 1976.

DOMINATOR 80

The first model of the legendary Dominator range. First produced in 1970, together with the larger Dominator 100, these combines were harvest giants in their day. Designed to meet the demand for larger machinery as a result of increasing acreages, it had a 3400 litres grain tank, which meant it could be driven for some time before unloading, and it was the first CLAAS combine to have hydrostatic ground drive. By now, the driver's platform was becoming more spacious compared to earlier models, and more function monitors appeared. On the Dominator 80 monitors were introduced to show the rotation speed of the feed housing elevator and straw walkers, together with the grain and returns elevators, and there were now electronic loss monitors for straw walkers and sieves. The first comfort cabs appeared on this range, with heating and ventilation. Engines were Mercedes or Perkins, 120hp, with a standard 15ft header, and on the 80, there was an option of hydrostatic and mechanical drive.

— LEFT

Seen on a farm at Lechlade near Cirencester, this Dominator 80, once worked annually until being abandoned and sadly awaits the fate of the scrap yard.

— BELOW

Dominator 85 in scrap yard at dealers. This combine has worked in the Much Wenlock area all its life, now redundant, it awaits its fate in the yard at Morris Corfield local Claas dealer. The engine may be removed to keep another older machine running. This model was launched in 1974, similar to the Dominator 80, but it had the new Claas ISS Intensive Separation System above the straw walkers. This was added to larger Senator and the Dominators. Machines with this fitted were identified by a '5' instead of the '0' as previously. The Dominator '5' series was the first to have pre-selected cutting height offered, where the header returned to a programmed preset height after each turn on a headland.

GARANT

The Garant was launched in 1967, at a time when the pull type combine was coming to an end. Previous pull combines had been right angle crop flow types, Claas only introduced a straight flow trailed combine with the Garant.

— **BELOW**

Here, pulled by a Fordson Major Mr Harvey Beamond of Boraston demonstrates it at a harvest event at the local Tenbury Wells show. The Garant, capable of cutting 4 tons an hour on average in wheat, had an 8ft cutter bar and 18in diameter drum and was a one man operated 4 straw walker combine,

requiring a tractor with pto drive from 45hp to operate it.

The hydraulic control unit was fitted to the tractor within easy reach of the driver, through which he could control raise or lower pick up reel and cutter bar independent of each other and also engage the clutch for the grain tank. It was only marketed as a tanker model, but it could have a bagging off attachment at the end of the unloading auger, or a side platform when the grain is taken from the bottom of the tank. The grain tank could hold 50 bushels or 25 cwt of wheat. Cost in 1967 was £1,650 for an 8 foot cut model.

COMPACT 25

— **RIGHT**

This one has been converted for use as a plot combine for harvesting crops in trials at Aberystwyth University. They had headers of 7ft and 8ft and were powered by a 45hp 4 cylinder diesel engine. They had five straw walkers and the drum size was 18in diameter and 38in wide, with a grain tank holding 31 bushels. Because of their compact design, they were often converted for use as plot combines, like this one at Aberystwyth University Department of Agriculture. A bagging off device at the grain tank outlet could be added as an option for grain. samples from trials plots.

CONSUL

The Consul was introduced in 1967 and sold alongside the Cosmos, it featured new styling which was introduced with the Senator. The Comet and Corsar followed. The Consul was built until 1981.

This combine had been moved from a hill farm above Painscastle on the Welsh borders to save it from the scrap merchant for £250, and is in my own collection.

A self propelled combine for the smaller acreage farmer, this had an 8ft 6in cut, four straw walkers, grain tank capacity of 2000 litres, or 55 bushels, or 31 cwt wheat and was powered by a 4 cylinder, about 68hp engine, situated to the side of the driver, with hydraulic steering. It was a medium size combine, sold alongside the Senators, Compact and Dominator. The drum width was 42in and diameter was 18in/450mm. This threshing drum size was standard on Claas combines. The unloading tube was swung into position manually. Straw chopper and cab were optional. Few of these models were sold in the UK. It was also offered with a 10ft header, cost of a Consul new in 1976 with 8ft 6in header was £11,800, a 10ft model cost £12,160.

— LEFT
Consul in barn awaits restoration.

PROTECTOR 6

Working at Penywrlodd Farm above Clyro, Hay-on-Wye Herefordshire, a smaller version of the Senator, the Protector was launched in 1968 and manufactured until 1972. The standard model had an 8½ ft header, 4 cylinder 72hp Perkins Diesel engine and 55 bushel grain tank. There were also models with 10ft headers, and 68 hp engines. (According to sales brochures most were 4 cylinder 72hp engines) It also featured the new styling and colour, introduced with the Senator range, with similar features such as hydrostatic steering, and hydraulic controls - one lever on the hydraulic control unit adjusts the cutter bar and reel height, drum speed and forward speed. (The Protector 4 and 6 were later versions denoting 4 and 6 cylinder engines).

DOMINATOR 76

The '6' series Dominators consisting of the 56, 76, 98 and 106, were launched in 1978. The cab was still listed as optional in sales brochures of this period, but for the first time became an integral part of the machine, with option of ventilation and or heating and air conditioning. There was more emphasis on driver comfort, an upholstered seat with adjustable suspension according to the drivers weight, now being standard. A 12ft cutter bar was standard, with options of 10ft and 13ft, and header trolleys for transport were offered amongst the options. A 4 straw walker machine, it had a grain tank capacity of 4200 litres,

hydraulic grain discharge unloading augers became standard, and a 6 cylinder 120hp engine, which was now situated behind the drivers cab in front of the grain tank. Transmission was mechanical with hydrostatic option, steering was hydrostatic. A Manual version of the 76 cost £26,885 in September 1980.

This combine belongs to Mr David Rawlings and is working in winter barley at Greete, near Ludlow in Shropshire, this one cuts 120 acres a year, and harvests mainly wheat and barley for animal feed on a beef rearing farm.

DOMINATOR 96

This belongs to a farmer and contractor Keith Morris of Moat Farm, Orcop Herefordshire, and works alongside a Mega 204, harvesting in a mainly mixed farming and stock rearing area.

A five straw walker combine, this was the top of the '6' series range together with the 106. It retained the CLAAS 18in diameter drum, and had a grain tank capacity of 5200 litres, and 150hp engine with hydrostatic drive and transmission and had a newly designed mounted straw chopper. It had a cutting width of 15ft with option of 17ft. The CLAAS ISS system above the straw walkers was offered in the larger '6' models, the 96 and 106. Cost of

a Dominator 96 Manual model, De Luxe specification, with a cab, cooler, RDS Mk IV Monitor and grain tank beacon was £37,650 in September 1980.

DOMINATOR 96 H

Seen here working at Willstone Farm, Cardington near Church Stretton in Shropshire, this Dominator 96 H with 17ft header and Mercedes engine, was fitted with the CLAAS hillside kit, after it was purchased by Steve Pennington.

The fully automatic hillside levelling could cope with up to 36% working across hillsides and up to 22% working up an incline and up to 11% working down an incline. The cutter bar is mounted on a centrally positioned pivot. Steel cables running over rollers keep the cutterbar fully synchronized with the front axle according to the slope being encountered. An additional feed roll with guide plates ensures a continuous flow of material.

The automatic levelling control for side hill, and incline and decline work is achieved by means of 2 independent pendulums which are mounted in a dust proof casing. When the machine encounters changes in ground contours, the rear of the machine is automatically kept in a level plain. To prevent problems occurring, 2 fully independent hydraulic systems are used, one for working on side hill and the other for incline and decline work. The hydraulic cylinders for side hill levelling are positioned at the front of the machine, and the cylinders for up and down hill work are mounted on a pivoting frame at he rear. Lock up valves and double acting hydraulic cylinders prevent, even with a leaking hydraulic system, a change in the levelling of the combine. The H models were offered with hydrostatic transmission.

DOMINATOR 98 SL CLASSIC

Working at Turnastone Farm Vowchurch Hereford, in spring barley.

The first of the '8' series appeared in 1981, with the smaller 38 and 48 models, followed by the 78, 98 and 108.

A feature of the '8' series was the introduction of the Multifunction joystick, which was modelled on the joystick principle. It appeared on the '8' series on the 98 and 108, which were first produced in 1985. The driver now had the operating functions in one hand. Later versions of

the Dominator 98 were the Maxi and Classic. The Classic was produced in 1991, with the SL model being the hydrostatic version and S the manual drive. It was a five straw walker machine with Intensive Separation System over the walkers. Headers came in 3.9, 4.5 and 5.1m, with CLAAS Contour automatic ground pressure control system. By the 1980's, headers were becoming wider due to demand, so that a greater area of ground could be covered in an hour. More

combines such as the 98 and 108 were fitted with a header reverser, an auxiliary drive and clutch allowed the driver to reverse the header to discharge crop jams in the intake auger, without the tiring job of manually clearing it.

The grain tank held 5200 litres and it was powered by a Mercedes Benz OM366 A 170hp engine, the S manual model had a 160hp engine. The 3D system and straw chopper was offered as optional. List price in August 1991 for a 98 SL Classic with

3D sieves was £86,000, and £82,750 for a standard sieve model.

DOMINATOR 108S

Working here in the wet harvest of 2008, it cuts some Oilseed rape in between the showers near Orcop Herefordshire.

The 108 was added to the '8' series in 1985, and was available as a Manual S model or hydrostatic SL model. A 15ft header was standard with 20ft optional.

By the 1980's, hydrostatic transmission was often offered as an option, and by the 1990's it became standard on combines. This gave an infinitely variable selection of forward speeds allowing for greater flexibility and higher output.

The cab was fitted with air conditioning with heating now and ease of operation aswell as driver comfort were improved, with the new multi function control lever and improved monitoring of machine functions, to increase machine performance. This model and others in the '8' series were offered with the CLAAS 3D dynamic slope compensation as an option, this had been introduced on the CS range.

There was an electric header reverser and electric cutting height indicator and the Claas Contour system, which is the cutter bar automatic ground pressure sensing system. Grain tank capacity increased to 6500 litres and the 108 S seen here cutting some OSR in the wet harvest of 2008, had a 180hp 6 cylinder Perkins engine, while the SL model had a 6 cylinder Mercedes 221hp engine. The CLAAS drum diameter 450mm was retained. Drum Width was 1.58m. Chaff spreader, and straw choppers were optional. This model had a turbine fan adjusted from the cab, while the smaller models had a radial fan.

DOMINATOR MEGA 204

The Dominator Mega was launched for the 1993 harvest, with the 218 and 208. The same year, CLAAS introduced the APS system, which appeared on the Dominator Mega 208 and 218 models, and brought about a 30% increase in throughput. The APS system is still used today in the LEXION range, which is an additional accelerator drum and pre separation concave, installed ahead of the main threshing drum, unlike other manufacturers. The accelerator drum speeds up the flow of the crop, before the material passes to the drum. Centrifugal forces in the threshing unit are increased, and aids early grain separation by the concave under the accelerator drum. The 202, 203 and 204 followed in 1994. Auto Contour was standard on the 218, and an option on the other Dominator Mega models. The Mega 204 was offered with 5.10m to 6.00m (20ft) headers. Powered by a Mercedes Benz OM366LA 200hp engine, this model was a five straw walker combine, it was a hydrostatic drive model with grain tank volume of 6200 litres and options of the 3D cleaning system. A straw chopper and spreader were now standard, rather than an option. As more combines were fitted with straw choppers, extra engine power was needed. The newly designed VISTA cab was offered on the later Dominator Mega models in 1995.

The last year of production of the Dominator Mega range was 1995, when it was replaced by the Lexion range. Other more sophisticated controls were offered, including Yield-o-meter as an option, and CEBIS, the CLAAS computer based control first appeared on the Mega models as an option. This is for monitoring, registration and giving information on machine data, from which adjustments can be made. Data can also be printed out.

— ABOVE

A 204 owned by Keith Morris of Moat Farm Orcop, Herefordshire. It cuts wheat barley and oats on the mixed dairy farm and does some local contract work in this mainly stock rearing area.

MEDION 310

This Medion 310, a five straw walker combine is working at Greete, near Ludlow in Shropshire. It is one of three models launched in 2001 to replace the Mega 350 and 360 and the Dominator series. The others were the 330 and 340. They followed on from the Dominator style of combines, with features such as the ISS Intensive Separation System,

Multi finger intake auger, CLAAS Auto Contour, and all automatic cutter bar control, with cutting widths of C660M, C750M and C900M. It also had the APS threshing system. It has the Vista cab, with more sophisticated option such as Agrocom Control terminal the interface for yield metering. There was new engine technology on this model, the minimum

fuel consumption was achieved by the use of high pressure injection technology with solenoid controlled injection pumps for each cylinder, with electric engine management. The grain tank is 5800 litres and it is powered by a Daimler Chrysler (Mercedes) OM 906 LA 6 cylinder 204hp engine. 3D sieves were offered as an option.

LEXION 430

Following the launch of the first Lexion, the 480 in 1996, the 405 to 460 followed. First year of production was 1997. The Lexion 430 has proved to be a very popular size combine for the medium size farmer and contractor in Western areas of Britain.

— LEFT

This Lexion 430, belonging to a contractor in the Llangorse area of the Brecon Beacons National park in Wales, has the green undercarriage of the earlier Lexions, and is seen here cutting spring barley in the damp conditions of the 2008 harvest, late in September, near Llangorse, Brecon.

— BELOW

The Lexion 430 is seen cutting wheat near Credden Hill it belongs to contractor Mervyn Synnock from Weobley, Hereford. The sales brochure for a 430 lists Auto Contour 6.0m/20ft as standard, with options of 18ft or 22ft, but on the smaller models, 420, 410 and 405, Contour cutter bars were standard. A five straw walker combine, it has the APS System, with synchronised impeller as standard, Drum Diameter of 600mm and width of 1420mm, 4 turbine fans controlled from the cab. It has a 7800 litre grain tank, and is powered by 240hp a Mercedes Benz engine, later models were Caterpillar engines 256 maximum hp. The early Lexions had a green undercarriage, whilst later models changed to black. Options were 3 D sieves, Quantimeter yield metering and printer and straw chopper.

— **Main Image**

View of Lexion 430 from rear in OSR.

— **Above**

This 430 has the Vista cab and standard Contour cutter bar of 18ft and this machine is a contractors combine working at Acton Scott Farm, where it is cutting winter barley for Mr Edward Jones on a modern mixed farm adjoining Acton Scott Historic Farm Musuem, where , in contrast horses and a binder cut the harvest as in Victorian times.

LEXION 450
LEXION 450 in OSR WITH VARIO HEADER

— **Above Right**

Seen working at Ivington near Leominster, Herefordshire it belongs to a local contractor.

Vario cutter bars were launched in 1998 for Lexion 25 and 30ft headers. The Vario was developed for situations where the length of the table needs to be adjusted on the move, in response to differing crops. The setting is changed at the touch of a button in the cab in a range from 100mm shorter to 200mm longer. However the crop is standing, it aids higher output. The Vario cutter bar can be extended still further to harvest OSR. The vertical knife is fitted and additional cover plates are fitted across the width of the cutter bar table. It had a straw chopper with push button engagement from rear of the combine and a folding chaff spreader.

— **Below Right**

This Lexion 450 has a standard Auto Contour 6.6m /22ft header, with the options being 6.0m/20ft and 7.5m/ 25ft. The Auto Contour guidance system had automatic reel adjustment, and automatic speed and height adjustment for the reel. It is cutting organic spring barley for Mr Robertson on a farm where all cereals are grown organically, at Acton Reynald, Shropshire, owned by contractor David Eggerton, and cuts about 1200 acres annually.

A six straw walker machine with ISS system over the walkers, it has a straw chopper and chaff spreader with push button engagement. The chaff spreader is folded up for easy access to the sieves. The grain tank holds 8600 litres, approx 6.8 tonnes of wheat and it is powered by a Caterpillar C9 engine maximum hp of 299hp. It was offered with options of 3D sieves, and Quantimeter with moisture meter. From 1999, Laser pilot was optional.

LEXION DECALS

The Lexion 430 has the decals in red letters, the first version on the Lexion, before they changed to black on the Lexion 450,

The Lexion 520 shows the present form of decals on the 500 Series.

LEXION 480

The Lexion 480 was the first in the Lexion family, launched in 1995 and first produced in 1996 and marked the beginning of a long line of revolutionary combines, where electronics had taken over the main control and monitoring functions completely, with the CEBIS-CLAAS Electronic On Board Information System. Basic machine settings were built into the system, drum speed, concave, fan speed sieves were automatically set but could be overridden by the driver and stored in the memory. Enhanced operator comfort and increased throughput made this the highest capacity combine on the market. The other main feature of this model was that it was the first of the 'hybrid' models, the conventional threshing system combined with the introduction of two rotors fitted lengthways, known as Roto Plus. The CLAAS APS system used on the Mega models was retained. The drum diameter was increased to 600mm from 450mm for the first time.

The Lexion 480 seen here with Vario 7.50 cutter bar with laser pilot, is cutting winter wheat in the difficult harvest conditions of 1978, near Pencome, Bromyard, Herefordshire, on a misty day in late September. It is one of a fleet of combines run by local contractor A Legge and Sons. The grain tank holds 10,500 litres and a new engine was introduced on this model, a Mercedes Benz 400hp unit. Once the highest capacity combine on the market, the 480 cut 40 tonnes an hour achieving a harvesting record one year. Combines had moved on from the days of the Claas SF which was then a high capacity machine cutting 4 tonnes an hour.

The Lexion 480 has the newly designed Straw chopper and Uni spreader for the Lexion 480. The spreading fans of the Uni spreader blow the straw and chaff over the wider width of the cutter bars on the Lexion range, with a characteristic tail wagging action.

Laser Pilot automatic guidance system, won an award at Agritechnica 1999, this was a breakthrough on the Lexion range. The visual unit of the Laser pilot is mounted in a housing above the left hand side of the cutter bar. Pulses of light are grouped in a sensor and transmitted to a point ahead of the machine. A second sensor picks up the impulses as they are reflected back from the standing crop and stubble and measures the return times. The system can recognise the dividing line and steers the combine automatically along this line.

LEXION 470

The Lexion 470, a rotary combine powered by a Caterpillar 9 339hp engine. It was the last of the 400 series, and was launched in 2001 for the following harvest, it paved the way for the introduction of the 500 series.

Here, an immaculately maintained example with 7.50m/25ft Vario header and laser pilot, cuts in region of 900 acres of winter wheat annually at J G Goring Ltd, Dorstone, Herefordshire. This one here has a Quantimeter yield metering device, listed as an option in the sales brochure. Although similar to the other 400 series Lexions, the 470 came with a few changes, which were carried over to the new 500 series. A new design multi function lever

with more functions on the joystick, including grain discharge and unloading auger functions, a newly designed steering column, and new features in the Vista cab - a new air conditioning system, were amongst innovations. The twin rotors were redesigned, including an optional rotor variator allowing in cab changes, whist other models this remained manually adjustment. It was a popular machine for contractors, due to

its narrower width than the larger Lexion 480, which gives it easier road mobility, but at the same time offered high capacity. The 470 has a grain tank capacity of 9600 litres. Other cutting widths offered were 6.0m/20ft and 6.60m/22ft. Vario Cutter bars, introduced in 1998, enable the table length to be moved on the go from the cab, from 10cm shorter than standard to 20cm longer.

FLEET OF CLAAS COMBINES

Fleet of Claas combines belonging to contractor Alan Johnson of Tarleton Lancashire cutting winter oats on first day of harvest.

A Lexion 510, Lexion 460, two Lexion 430's and a Mega 204 make up the fleet. These combines are impeccably maintained.

LEXION 460 EVOLUTION

This Evolution six straw walker combine with C 660 Auto Contour 22ft header, straw chopper and chaff spreader, is cutting winter barley near Greete, Ludlow, Shropshire. Launched in 2001 for the 2002 season, the Evolution models offered a higher specification premium product range and were sold alongside the standard Lexion models.   The main feature was the new MSS - Multi Seperator System, as standard above the straw walkers instead of ISS, this aerated the straw more efficiently and improved the crop flow in heavier yields of over 10 tons an acre which were now becoming common, and in damper greener crops. New cab features including climate control and a new steering column, and a new style multi function control lever as on the 470. Engine power was increased and changed to a more fuel efficient Caterpillar 330hp engine, designed with a fuel efficient engine management system, which controls the fuel lettering solenoids, so that the amount of fuel injected is exactly right for the prevailing conditions. The grain tank has a capacity of 6500 litres. Tracks were offered as an option from 2003.

LEXION 510

The Lexion 500 series was introduced in 2003 for the 2004 harvest, The models were introduced with some new features, some as options, such as dust extraction on the feeder housing seen on the Evolution models, New Vario header, a single multi coupler attachment which makes the fixing and removal of the header quicker and change to Caterpillar engines, introduced on the Evolution models. The Vista cab with increased space and reduced noise levels was redesigned, and the multi function lever joystick now has Vario controls added to it, plus Instant Stop cutter bar brake, discharge auger swivelling and off loading,

and right hand Laser Pilot is available as an option. Electronic gear shifting, with push button selections were also introduced on the 500 Series.

The baby of the Lexion family, this five straw walker combine with standard C540 18ft header and Caterpillar C6 - 6 cylinder 235hp engine, and 7300 litre grain tank. It is a more basic specification model of this range, with paddle rather than turbine type fan, standard header and Standard cut chopper. A Quantimeter, Yield monitor and 3D sieves are offered as options. A standard Lexion 510 with C 5.4m header has a list price of £166,670 for 2010 harvest.

This Lexion 510, one of a fleet of five CLAAS combines, cuts some winter oats on the first day of harvest, for contractor Alan Johnson from Tarleton near Southport, Lancashire.

LEXION 530 MONTANA

A very popular size Lexion for the medium size farmer with difficult roads and field sizes to negotiate, this combine here, cutting OSR at Bitterley Ludlow in Shropshire, has a Vario 6.60m header with the Vario header extended for cutting OSR. It is a five walker machine, with

Caterpillar C9 6 cylinder 295hp engine using electronic management, grain tank capacity of 8600 litres and has 3D slope compensation.

— **ABOVE AND OPPOSITE**

Roger Benbow from Much Wenlock Shropshire is cutting winter wheat in a 530 Montana here - on undulating ground on the Culmington Estate, near Craven Arms, Shropshire. This model has a Vario 750 - 7.60m header.

The Montana model, the CLAAS hills side combine was first introduced in 2002 for the 2003 harvest, on the Lexion 430 Evolution and 470 Evolution. The header mounting system of the Montana allows Auto Contour cutter bar to move independently of the elevator, so the required cutting height can be maintained. The Montana front axle has a cam type final drive, that can be rotated by hydraulic rams, so that the combine can remain level on slopes of 17%, giving the same performance as on level fields with uniform stubble height.

— **LEFT**

Lexion 530 chopping oilseed rape at Bitterley, Ludlow, Shropshire.

LEXION 550 MONTANA

Seen here cutting winter barley in Worcestershire, this 6 straw walker Lexion 550 Montana powered by a Caterpillar C9 6 cylinder 351hp engine with electronic management has a Vario 660 22ft header and grain tank capacity of 9600 litres, and cuts in the region of 2000 acres annually on a large potato and arable farm. Specification is similar to the other straw walker Lexions, but it has a wider axle. Header options for this model are C or Vario 450, up to 9.00 - 9.12m, although 22ft and 25ft are the most popular for this size.

LEXION 570+MONTANA

BEAT THE STORM

— **Opposite**

Farmer contractor John Fox cuts OSR in the catch harvest, between the storms in 2008.

This Lexion 570+ Montana with a Vario 7.5m/25ft header, is cutting Castille oilseed rape, grown for producing rape seed oil, at John Davies Farms, Swancote, Bridgnorth, Shropshire, during the catchy harvest of 2008.

New for the 2006 season, it is a slightly higher spec model than the 570, introduced to provide higher power after the 570 was discontinued, it is sold alongside a lower spec 570C. Powered by a Caterpillar C 13 445hp engine, it is said to be capable of clearing 1400 to 1800 acres a season. As it is geared to

help the machine cover greater areas, in addition to increased engine power, it is equipped with a power spreader as standard, and VRS-Variable Rotor Speed to adjust the Roto-Plus rotors, as well as a grain meter. Here Mr John Fox, local farmer and contractor is working at John Davies Farms, Swancote, Bridgnorth in Shropshire with a Lexion 570+Montana, and cuts on average 1300 acres of OSR and winter wheat a season, much of it very hilly terrain.

The main feature of the Montana is a three dimensional multi-contour control system for keeping a constant output at whatever angle. The whole combine including the driver stays level, it has a

lateral compensation of up to 17% and fore and aft compensation up to 6%. The Montana has multi contour functions. The combines three dimensional control of the swivelling cutter bar frame and the cutter bar angle relative to the axle position, combine with all the features of the Auto Contour Control. The control system serves the horizontal alignment of the combine on slopes. The control unit is connected to an inclinometer (electronic spirit level). When the inclinometer signals a deviation from the horizontal position, the slope control system can level the machine by hydraulically retracting or extending the front wheels, When the Montana is set on Automatic

mode, it then always stays in a level position. regardless of the type of ground.

A Differential lock comes with the Montana model, to give full traction on steep slopes. The Montana also features an exclusive Overdrive transmission design, with two speed electro hydraulic shift gear box. The overdrive changes its torque range and downshifts automatically when loading increases.

Header options for this model are from 6.0m to 10.50m/30 feet. Powered by a Caterpillar C13 6 cylinder engine of 455hp, designed to meet emission standards, Euromot 14 a Standard, its fuel tank holds 800 litres and grain tank capacity is 10,500 litres. (Latest combines

now have engines to meet Euromot 111a emissions compliance) The Jet Stream cleaning system on this model ensures a higher wind pressure than other systems, this is generated by 6 electrically operated turbine fans with two separate wind channels. The long compensation channel beneath the removable preparation floor ensures a more uniform wind pressure and more efficient cleaning quality. Jet Stream has a higher dual ventilated step. A Quantimeter comes as standard and left and right laser pilot for the header is an option. The Special Cut 11 Chopper with additional knives is standard on the Montana with a Power Spreader which this machine has.

Unloading winter barley

With increasing header widths, the discharge augers of combines have become longer, when grain is unloaded on the move, the tractor has to keep alongside the header, enabling the trailer to be in the right position for the grain to fill it. Models with wide headers are offered with options of longer auger lengths.

LEXION 570+MONTANA

This picture of John Fox's Lexion 570+Montana working on the steepest field at John Davies Farms Bridgnorth show the Montana combine in full action. This combine is also fitted with four wheel drive axle and 3D dynamic slope compensation. The local dealer sold fifteen four wheel drive kits during the summer of 2007 due to the wet harvest conditions.

The core element of the Montana is its driving axle. The final drive units of the front axle are turned upwards and downwards from the central position independently of each other by the hydraulic pivoting rams, in order to adjust the wheels in relation to the ground, and to compensate for the angle of the slope. The hydraulic rams are controlled by an electronic box mounted centrally on the drive axle. Output is transferred from the hydraulic motor to an electro hydraulically operated two speed gearbox. Power is transmitted to the wheels via a bevel gear drive and the final drive. This gives adaption for working on hilly terrain and better traction and operator comfort. Three Lexions at contractors yard await start of harvest.

— THIS PAGE
Two Lexion 570+'s cutting winter wheat in Worcestershire. Together with a Lexion 530, these cut in the region of 3000 acres in a season.

LEXION 570+TT

Special Cut 11 Chopper and Power Spreader are standard on the Terratrac, this 570+ Terractrac combine is on demonstration from the local Claas dealer, cutting Oilseed rape at a farm near Rochford, Tenbury Wells, Worcestershire, with an Oilseed rape attachment on a V 7.5 m header. An efficiently harvested field is the foundation for the next harvest. With an increase in minimal tillage equipment instead of the conventional plough, to prepare the new seedbed, developments in residual straw management have taken place, giving evenly short chopped straw and exact spreading over larger cutter bar widths. This Lexion has the Special Cut 11 Chopper with 108 knives, to finely chop the straw, which is then fed into the Power Spreader. With increased grain yields over recent years, the amount of straw grows along with it. A rapid and complete straw decomposition forms the basis for successful tillage systems.

Outputs vary upon weather conditions, crop straw quality amongst other factors but a 570+ achieved an average output of 40.39 tons an hour and 8.55 acres an hour or 3.46 ha an hour during trials in the wet 2008 harvest.

LEXION 580

LEXION 580 with 30ft header, wheeled version cuts winter wheat at Peter Vaughan's, Kingsland, Herefordshire, a large potato enterprise where wheat often follows potatoes in the arable crop rotation.

This features the Roto-Plus, Claas is the only manufacturer to use this method, known as the Hybrid system. The combination of conventional drums and independently speed adjusted rotors enabled one rotary Lexion to replace two 6 walker machines. The speed of the two rotors can be variably adjusted from the cab, VRS. Powered by a Daimler Chrysler V8 cylinder 462hp engine, Gross reserve power of 512hp, the 580 has a grain tank capacity of 10,500 litres

Cutting widths from 7.5m to 9.m are available for the 580 with standard left hand Laser pilot and optional right hand side. Earlier Lexion 580's had the Unispreader straw chopper and chaff spreader. This was replaced on later models by the Special Cut 11 chopper and power spreader. Quantimeter Yield metering and Yield mapping are Standard on this model.

LEXION 580+TT

Powered by a Mercedes Benz 517hp engine, the 580+ with V9.0m header retails at list price of £324,590 in Autumn of 2009, while a Terratrac model sells for £366,400 with V10.5 header.

Here, this Lexion 580+TT combine with 30ft header and laser pilot, is working at G C Davies & Co farm at Red House, Little Ness, Montford Bridge, Shrewsbury. Terratracs have increased in popularity since two wet harvests of 2007 and 2008. The Terratrac rubber belt drive keeps the width of the Lexion 580 down to 3.5metres. A new suspension on the Terratrac combine smooths out bumps and shocks on the road and in the field, reducing bouncing of the header and combine, and also reducing soil compaction. The large contact area reduces the ground pressure to less than half that of a combine fitted with oversize 1050 tyres.

A high capacity combine, the 580+ can achieve on spot outputs of 56.90 tons an hour and averaged 43.10 tons an hour and the average of 10.02 acres an hour during a wet harvest in 2008.

LEXION 600 35 FT HEADER

The most powerful combine in the world, with the highest throughput in the world when launched, it was first introduced in 2005 for the harvest of 2006, initially with a V900 30ft header, the emphasis was on further technology, and increased comfort in the Vista cab with automatic climate control, electronic hydrostatic system and overdrive transmission. It is offered with a choice of Laser pilot for the left as standard and an option for the right hand side or GPS Pilot, which uses signals from the global positioning system to automatically guide the Lexion along the edge of the crop. A new throughput regulator Cruise Pilot is standard, which measures the crop height in the front elevator while detecting the engine load and adapts the driving speed to the crop

conditions, enabling the combine to be driven to its limit. Other innovations on the 600 include new feed rake to handle increased throughput and Auto Contour 11 for the header, which regulates the ground pressure more concisely using a new cutter bar cylinder. Electronic sensors detect the hydraulic pressure automatically adjusting to suit the cutter bar weight and adjusts to suit the ground contours. A new design 7/18 concave with 7mm wire spacing in the first four rows and 18mm in the rear concave area aids maximum separation. Roto Plus technology was on the other Lexion rotaries is continued, only newly developed high performance rotors are used

LEXION 600 V1050 HEADER WILTSHIRE

Here a Lexion 600 from Germany with V1050 35ft header seen on demonstration on a road run, having previously worked in Hungary earlier in the season. It is cutting wheat near Swindon Wiltshire in 2007, when the V1050 header was launched. Powered by a V8 cylinder Mercedes Benz 16 litre engine, maximum 586hp, it holds 12,000 litres of grain in the tank.

Yield mapping, Quantimeter, Special Cut 11 Straw chopper and power spreader are all standard. Jet Stream cleaning system used on the 570 is retained, only with 8 turbine fans. Large 1,050/50R 32 front tyres could be fitted and Terratrac with suspension is an option.

Telematics, enables a combine to be monitored for performance from anywhere where there is internet access, by using an on board data logger to record selected information copied form the CAN BUS system on the combine every 15 seconds. it is stored on a PCMCIA card in CEBIS,. Every 15 seconds an on board modem calls a data transfer station and downloads the machines data to the internet, the data is stored on a secure server which can then be accessed viewed and analysed via the internet.

— **BELOW LEFT**

Lexion 600 V1050 Header coming straight to camera on demonstration from Germany working for dealer Morris Corfield of Much Wenlock, Shropshire.

LEXION 600 TT WITH V1250 HEADER

— **Below Right**

A prototype V1200 40ft header on this Lexion 600TT working at Ben Smiths Manor Road Farm, Wantage, Oxfordshire in August 2009. Driver Steve Rackham cuts winter wheat. This header was launched at Agritecnica, Hannover, Germany for the 2010 harvest.

— **Above Right**

Lexion 600TT with V1200 header on demonstration near at Yatesbury, Caine, Wiltshire through Claas dealers Mill Engineers and Vaughan Agri driven by Ludger Budde, from the marketing demonstration team at Harsewinkel, Germany.

The Lexion 600 has an enormous capacity, as an example, a Lexion 600 can cut enough wheat in a day to produce one million loaves of bread. List price of a Lexion 600TT with a 10.5 Vario header is £424,280 as at 2009.

TUCANO 430

Tucano 430 on demonstration near Swindon on a Road Run, in 2007, prior to it launch on the market for the following harvest.

TUCANO 480

Tucano 480 at Yatesbury, Caine, Wiltshire on demonstration during the 2009 harvest cutting wheat, with a V750 header, it is powered by a Caterpillar C9 built to comply with the latest Emissions Euromot 111 a standard, 8.8 litres 355hp engine, it has a grain tank capacity of 9000 litres.

A single rotor combine, the core component of the Lexion, the hybrid system is adapted to the size of the Tucano, using a Tangenital threshing system with APS combined with the Roto plus residual grain separation system. The single rotor has a larger diameter.

3D levelling is an option. Designed as a midrange combine offering farmers rotary technology at a lower cost then the Lexion. During tests in wheat, it achieved outputs of 4.3ha an hour and over 35 ton an hour. It comes with spacious Vista cab and Cebis screen with multifunction control lever similar to the Lexion. It is offered with header widths of V 900m to V 540m or with the standard C Contour Headers.

The Tucano 480 was launched at Agritechnica 2009 for the next harvest with a list price tag of £224,240, with a 6.60m header and Activ Spreader.

AVERO 320

Launched at Agritechnica in 2009, but on trial during the previous harvest in UK, it fills a gap between the smallest Tucano model and the older Dominator models, and designed for the smaller farmer. A four straw walker combine, it adds the APS pre-separation technology using a pegged drum and concave in front of the main drum and concave, found in Claas's larger machines. The combine is basically conventional inside but with a smarter

looking skin and capable of a 20% higher output according to the manufacturer over the Dominators. Powered by a Caterpillar C6 6 cylinder engine of 198hp, it has a 5600 litre grain tank and same roomy Vista cab as on the Tucano, with a more basic monitoring system than the Lexion, the CIS Claas Information System to monitor machine and engine functions. Headers are offered from 3.70m to 6.60m.

MASSEY HARRIS MASSEY FERGUSON

MH 726

Production of the 722 was phased out when it was transferred to the new MH factory in Kilmarnock where the MH 726 and MH 780 followed.

The 722 was succeeded by the 726 in the UK. The 726 had an 8ft 6in cutter bar, 2ft wide drum, 4 straw walkers and the option of a bagging off platform or grain tank. The 726 went into production at the new Kilmarnock factory in 1949. It had a Petrol/tvo six cylinder Austin Newage engine or a petrol Morris four cylinder unit of 56hp, and it had an electric table lift, as opposed to the manual lift of the No 21, This machine was the same as the No 26 in Canada, which had a 8ft 6in, or 12ft cut in a tanker or bagger version. From 1948, the 726 and 722 were the first combines to be fitted with on the move variable speed transmission, which was undertaken via a belt operating on variable pulleys. Most models were bagger versions, but a few

tanker models holding 40 bushels of grain were sold. Production ceased in 1953 when the 780 was launched.

This combine was lent to AGCO in France, for their celebration of 50 years of Massey Ferguson in 2008.

MH 750

This MH 750 is in the collection of Vintage combine enthusiast and collector, Mr Ron Knight of Great Casterton, Stamford Lincolnshire where it has been restored to working order. The 750 was launched by MH in the UK which was based on the trailed 'Clipper' combine, a tanker or bagger model, which was made in the USA, The Clipper was introduced with 4ft 6in, 6ft and 7ft cutting widths and made in the

USA at the Batavia plant in New York.

Production started on the 750 trailed bagger combine in 1953, but this did not sell much. A British version of the No 50, it had a 5ft cut with a Standard vaporising engine, transport width was 8ft 6in. It cost £725 for a 5ft 6in cut model in 1953 and was aimed at the farmer with smaller acreages. It had a TVO engine, and three spout bagger with a rotary screen to give

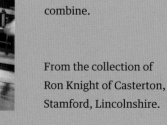

a good sample and in the sales brochure, it stated that it came with the new MH All Purpose Reel. A tractor of 25 to 30hp was required to pull the pto combine.

From the collection of Ron Knight of Casterton, Stamford, Lincolnshire.

MASSEY HARRIS 780 BAGGER

This MH 780 had worked in Herefordshire, it was first registered at a farm near Ross-on-wye and later worked near Almeley, Herefordshire. It was rescued for restoration by Philip Edwards from Pembridge area, for restoration. This MH 780 will be restored and hopefully work at the local Brimfield Working day to cut a few acres. In the 28 June 1996 issue of Farmers Weekly, a competition was launched to find the oldest working combine. This 780 was found to be the oldest combine still working. It is a bagger version with 8ft 6in header, four straw walkers and powered by an Perkins L4 4 cylinder 61hp engine. Models came with a choice of a Perkins L4 Diesel 4 cylinder 61hp engine, or by an Austin Newage 6 cylinder engine. The model was offered with options of a 10ft or 12 ft cutting width. After the 726, there were some innovations on the 780, which was launched for the 1954 harvest, including a new independent reel adjustment, new hydraulic speed control and hydraulic table lift, earlier 780 models had electric table lift. The drum was 22in diameter and the fuel tank held 20 gallons. The 780 was replaced by the 788 for the 1963 harvest. Price of Massey Harris 780 self propelled combine with 8½ cut was £1,525 for a diesel model in 1953, and £1,425 for a T.V.O. model.

M-H 780 SPECIAL TANKER MODEL

Available in cutting widths of 8ft 6in, 10ft or 12ft, this 8ft 6 in tanker model dating from 1958 was sold by E A Wilde of Hereford for £2,620, and is now at Tretire Court Farm, Pencoyd, Herefordshire, where it has spent much of its working life. It last worked about 25 years ago, It has an Austin Newage 6 cylinder 4 litre TVO engine, hydraulic table lift with manual reel adjustments, the reel bats were made of wood, as were the bearings for the four straw walkers. A wooden shaft drives the knife blade. The successor to the MH 780, it was basically the same, after the merger of MH with Ferguson, there were some improvements made to the 780 Special, it had a more advanced table lift, which now became hydraulic instead of the electric lift of the earlier 780's, and also speed control could be undertaken hydraulically: the transmission with hydraulic speed control meant that speeds could be changed immediately to suit different crops by selecting a notch with a variable speed lever. The reel could also be adjusted for height hydraulically from the drivers seat, and fore and aft adjustment was mechanical, instead of manually changing sprockets as on the earlier 780 models - but reel speed had to be changed with using alternative sprockets. The 780 Special was also available as a bagger version.

MH 735

The 735 introduced in 1956, was designed for the small farmer, with an overall width of 7ft 7in, it had a 6ft header, 4 cylinder 24hp Austin TVO or BMC Newage petrol engine with magneto ignition. A three straw walker machine, it came as either a bagger or tanker model, and had a 23in diameter drum. The table lift was hand operated. Farm safety regulations now began to show evidence, the user was advised to keep the spare sieves in their brackets to serve as safety guards for the belt and chain drives.

MASSEY FERGUSON TANKER 735

This also belongs to Kevin Norris, and is one of only two known to be still in existence. It had belonged to a contractor in Cambridgshire C E Whitehead, who ran it until 1970. It had been delivered new in 1956. It was then sold to a farmer in Llandrindod Wells, who cut 8 acres a year with it until 1980. It remained parked there until Kevin Norris rescued it in 2009 for restoration. It has a 32hp TVO Austin Newage engine. The bagger version is a Massey Harris, whilst this one is a Massey Ferguson model appearing a the time of the changeover from Massey Harris to Massey Ferguson. The Massey Harris models had yellow wheels, and white reel bats, whereas the Massey Ferguson 735's had grey wheels and red reel bats.

MASSEY HARRIS 735 BAGGER

This bagger version has an Austin Newage 1.5 litre BMC engine, which was the same as those used in the A55 cars, is seen working at Brimfield Vintage Club's Working day, and now belongs to a farmer and collector, Kevin Norris, near Alveley, Bridgnorth, Shropshire, who restored it. It once worked in mid Wales.

MF 400

Simon Jones of Ty Mawr Farm Llanigon near Hay on Wye has had this B reg 1964 MF400 since 1970, it completed its 38th consecutive harvest in 2008. Built at Kilmarnock, it has an 8ft 6in header. These combines were considered a high output machine in the 1960's, with outputs said to be in region of 5.5 tonnes an hour. The model was also offered with options of a 10ft or 12ft header, it was a four straw walker combine with 22in diameter drum. Following on from the 788, the MF combines now had safety guards and a more stylish exterior.

The MF 400 was powered by a Perkins A4 300 72hp diesel engine, made to MF specifications. In 1959, Perkins Engines of Peterborough was purchased by Massey Ferguson. Perkins had been the main supplier of diesel engines for Massey Ferguson for many years. Later in the 1990's, the then owner of Perkins LucasVarity was to sell off Perkins to Caterpillar Inc who is a major producer of large diesel engines in modern combines. When AGCO bought MF, the deal didn't include Perkins so the close link between the two brands formally ended although Perkins has continued as one of MF's key engine suppliers for tractors.

MF 500

The 400 and 500 marked the beginning of a new appearance and were now more stylish, guards hid moving belts and pulleys and the engine was situated higher out of the dust. Regulations regarding farm safety came into force, the Field Machinery regulations in 1965 meant that driving belts and chains had to be guarded, and function of levers clearly marked, hence manufactures fitted more elaborate guards on newly introduced machines, as well as better ladders for access to them. The twin saddle type grain tanks extended across the full width of the combine. The 500 differed from the 400 in that it had a bigger operators platform and the steps were behind the wheel with larger drive wheels. The grain auger was pivoted above the grain tank and was swung either manually or hydraulically according to the manufactures literature.

The yellow flash on the rotary air intake radiator screen was a feature of these MF combines, which dominated the harvest fields in the 1960's.

— **OPPOSITE PAGE**

This 500 still works near Preston on Wye Herefordshire where it cuts some barley for stock feed.

MF 510

Chris Ward bought this circa 1972 510 with 12ft cut from a farm sale near Hereford for £200 and still uses it to cut about 60 acres of wheat each year at Tretire Court, Pencoyd, Herefordshire. Once considered a high capacity combine, it was said to have an output of 8½ tonnes an hour. A six straw walker machine, these were manufactured from 1964/1965, they looked the same as the 500 but were wider with greater separating area, and featured the well known MF Quick Attach table. Header options were 10, 12, 14 or 16ft. Powered by a 104 hp Perkins A6.354 6 cylinder diesel engine, the two saddle type grain tanks had a combined capacity of 77 bushels. The grain unloading auger is now operated hydraulically.

MF 31

This one is in working order and belongs to a farmer and Vintage enthusiast Andrew Simmonds, at Pwllperran farm, Painscastle where it is in his collection of vintage tractors and combines. It is a three straw walker combine, is thought to have been made in the MF factory in Germany in the mid to late 1960's, designed for the smaller farmer. It is D registered has a 7 foot header, with overall transport width of only 8ft 6ins, it was very compact. Powered by a Perkins A4 107 4 cylinder Diesel engine of 39hp, an unusual feature is that it has concealed ballast pockets in the rear hood, so that sand could be used as counterbalance in place of cast weights on the steering wheels as used on the earlier 735, as being so light in weight, they could easily lose their centre of gravity. Capable of harvesting 2 tons an hour, it had a grain tank of 18½ imperial bushels. It was also offered as a bagger version and was sold alongside the 515 Multi Flow model and the 410 and 510 models, and to begin with the 788.

MF 515 MULTI-FLOW

The Kilmarnock built 510 and 515 combines typified the style of the 400 and 500 models, but the 515 combine was larger with a wider separating area, the 515 having an exclusive double action separator which enhanced the separation of grain from the straw. Weighing over 5 tons, it was marketed alongside the 410, 415 and the new MF 187 in the 1970 product list.

This MF 515 with a 10ft header came from a farm near Bucknall near Knighton on the Welsh borders, and now belongs to a collector. It was introduced in the mid 1960's and in 1970 this model was the largest MF combine on the market in the UK, with an output of up to 10 tons an hour. It was also offered with header options of 12ft, 14ft and 16ft, with a Quick Attach table and automatic table height control. In 1970, Automatic table height control was offered as a new feature whereas on the previous 410 and 415 models, it was an option. The 515 that year was also offered with new safety guards including filled in reel spiders, at this time there was becoming more emphasis on farm safety. The table was counter balanced by an hydraulic accumulator and the reel was hydraulically adjusted for and aft and for height and speed. It had a cylinder width of 45in and diameter of 22in and was a six straw walker combine.

A feature of the 515 was the Multi Flow System, a MF secondary separation system, first seen on the 415. With the Double Action Separating system, additional separation occurs as the grain falls clear of the straw walkers on to a pan. Grain then goes through a wire comb onto an auger below a rotor, from where it is elevated to a pan under the walkers to the top sieve.

The 515 also had the rethresher, which could be used as a slinger or rethresher. This discharges the returns on to the straw walker pan. It has double ended paddle arms and a serrated concave and blanking plate. Unripe heads or barley awns which were too large to pass through the sieve were augered to the rethresher, so eliminating rethreshing though the main cylinder. This was an MF feature.

The 515 had a Perkins A6 354 Direct injection 6 cylinder diesel engine of 104hp built to MF specifications and a rotary self cleaning radiator air intake screen. The yellow swirl on the rotating screen was a feature of the MF combines of the 1960's and early 1970's. Power assisted steering was standard.

The grain tank held 77 bushels or 2790 litres approximately 43 cwt of wheat in those days, in two saddle tanks.

The 515 was built at Kilmarnock and was evantualy replaced by the 525.

MF 525

This model has the Multi Flow seen at rear of the combine. It still cuts about 20 acres of barley a year on a stock rearing farm near Vowchurch, Herefordshire, where it has spent all its life within a few miles of the district since it was new. It has a 10 foot header, and one of he features of the model is the MF High Inertia drum, which is wider with diameter of 22in and heavier built than conventional low inertia drums which were 18in diameter. The spider wheels to which the rasp bars are attached are made of stronger steel, the drum was able to work at a slower speed. It also has the MF Multi Flow System. The 'Multi Flow' first seen on the 515 was a secondary Double Action Separation system, which appeared on the 515. On the rear of the combine, streamlined into the main bodywork, the Multi Flow unit was fitted. This feature allowed the straw coming off the walkers to pass down a steep pan with metal combs in the bottom. As grain is freed from the straw coming off the walkers, it falls through a comb, a rotary beater knocked the straw against the pans as it passed through the comb onto the grain pan. - A sloping pan directs grain recovered at the final separation stage to auger trough at the foot of the multi flow separator at rear of combine

A Cross auger in the trough delivers the grain to an elevator with a short cross auger at the top to deliver the final recovery grain to a pan under the straw walkers. A rotary beater shakes out any remaining grains before straw is thrown out from the combine at the rear.

The system allowed the combine to work faster and keep grain loss to a minimum. Most combines like this one were still sold without a cab at this time.

— **BELOW**
525 with cab.

This 12ft cut 525 has spent most of its life in Herefordshire, The cab was put on at a later date. At this time, many combines still did not have cabs, but they were offered on the 625 model. It still cuts around 60 acres of oats and barley and some wheat on a stock farm near Dorstone, Hereford.

Introduced in 1971 to replace the 510/515 series, it was offered with cutter bar widths of 10ft, 12ft and 14ft, and had the MF Quick Attach table, and was powered by a Perkins A6-354 6 cylinder diesel engine of 104hp. The grain tank held 83 bushels. The drivers platform was still offset to the left of the combine.

MF 187

This MF 187 combine manufactured in 1970, with a ten foot cut, still harvests thirty acres every year near Ludlow Shropshire, where it has worked since 1976, cutting winter oats and wheat for a mixed stock farm. When new it cuts about 150 acres a year at a farm near Ditton Priors, Bridgnorth.

Designed to harvest crops of up to 3 acres an hour, it came with options of 8ft 6in or 10ft headers, with wobble box knife drive. Fore and aft reel spped was mechanically adjusted and height control hydraulically operated from the drivers seat. On the 1970 model, a new telescopic header where an 8ft 6in header could expand to 10ft was available. Powered by a Perkins A4 236 direct injection 4 cylinder 69hp diesel engine, it was a three straw walker machine with grain tank capacity of 60 bushels. Introduced to the UK market in 1970, it was made in the MF factory at Marquette in France. Some of the parts were interchangeable with the larger 487 model. The 187 and 487 had the same layout as the earlier 500's, which were still available at this time.

MF 307

This 307 combine in a West Midlands scrap yard was built at Marquette in France and replaced the 187.

MF 307 AND 506

Smaller combines for the smaller farmer were made in France and sold in the UK. These included the MF 307 which was launched for the 1975 season replacing the 187, and the 487 Special was replaced by a restyled 506. The 307 was larger than the 187, and came with a Perkins 77hp A4.236 engine, larger grain tank and hydrostatic instead of mechanical drive. An 8ft 6in model cost £5,870 and a 10ft cut model cost £6,020 in 1975. The 506 cost £7,750 for a 12ft cut model, or £7,670 for a 10ft Quick Attach table.

— **ABOVE**

Rescued from a farm on the Welsh borders near Llangorse, Brecon, this combine had not been used for some years, it was left redundant in a field.

MF 240

At Acton Scott Farm, Church Stretton, Shropshire, this Massey Ferguson 240 combine belongs to Mr. Edward Jones and is now nearly thirty years old, replaced an MF 307, and still cuts a few acres of mainly oats each year, usually in small fields where the contractors large combine finds it difficult to access. It came new to the farm in August 1982, when it cut 130 acres a year. It was sold by Massey dealers Shukers of Shrewsbury, costing in the region of £22,000, there were not many of these combines made. It replaced the 307 model which had been launched in 1974 for the following harvest and was designed for the smaller farmer. A three straw walker combine, this one has a 10ft fixed header, although an option of 8ft 6inch was available, and it was powered by a Perkins A4.236 direct injection 4 cylinder 68hp diesel engine, and had a 83 bushel capacity grain tank. As with all Massey combines from the MH 726 until the later models, the driver's platform was offset to the left, rather than being centrally situated.

Note the driver is wearing an 'AIRSTREAM' helmet, which was popular about 15 to 20 years ago, for use in grain stores, and for use on tractors and combines before cabs became common place. This was a fibre glass safety helmet, made by Racal. It had a transparent visor that covered the head. A battery operated fan blew filtered air into the helmet, and the pressure generated kept the dust out, allowing the wearer to breathe in clean air.

MF 760

In October 1973, two 760's were brought from Canada for trial in European conditions, one was working near Ancaster Lincs, It was claimed that the 760 could do the work of three 625's and average five to six acres an hour. It was claimed at the time to be the biggest combine ever made in North America, with 5ft wide and 22in diameter High Inertia drum, with 24ft cutting widths, but in Europe these were 20ft. Rate of discharge from the 175 bushel grain tank was four tons in about two minutes.

One source says that the 760 was launched in N America in 1971 , a series of paddle elevators replaced the feed elevator, a system unique at the time to MF, which moved grain from the table up the elevator. The 700 machines were due to be replaced by the updated versions the 850 and 860 marketed in 1981.

It was built for the North American conditions, it was found to have limited capacity to separate grain from the straw in UK conditions. Modifications were made for European conditions to cope with the heavier straw in the crops, including a bigger engine and still longer straw walkers.

In 1974, when the 760 was introduced, it was the world's largest combine. Over 400 Brantford built MF 750 and MF 760 combines were in the UK by mid 1978.

— **ABOVE**

MF 760 in scrap dealers yard JMT Engineering, Bishops Itchington, Warwickshire.

The Brantford factory shipped 419 MF700 Series combines to Europe in the first half of 1978, with the UK having the lion's share of over 200 units.

Offered with header options of 18ft or 20ft initially, and later 16ft, the 760 was powered by a Perkins AT6.354 diesel 175hp engine. Straw chopper and spreader was an option. Most combines were still not fitted with engine hour meters, the 760 had one as an option. Price of a 760in November 1975 was £22,845 with a 20ft table.

MF 805

Priced at £35,770 for the 1984 harvest, this 805 combine was made in France, and was launched in 1983 for the following harvest, and was one of the 800 series launched to improve upon the existing 500 and 600 series. Cutter widths were available as 10ft and 12ft with the Quick Attach and New Profile Table. It had the MF High Inertia cylinder which was 22in diameter and Cascade Separator. The High Inertia cylinder was a feature of MF combines at this time, it immense weight gave it twice the threshing force of conventional cylinders, the spider shaped wheels to which the rasp bars are attached are made of thicker and stronger steel, the 22in cylinder could work at a slower speed than the 18 in diameter drums used on other makes. It was Powered by a Perkins A6 3544 6 cylinder diesel 104hp engine, it had an integral pressurised cab with air conditioning, and tinted glass, with high specification drivers seat and adjustable steering column. Driver comfort increased during the 1980's and more combines were being offered with an integral cab as part of the combine.

The 855 and 865 launched in N America in 1985, were available in Europe from late 1981, they used a cascade separator system that employed a beater to strip away grain from the straw as it fell from the end of the straw walkers.

The Brantford built 800 series were announced in UK in 1981 and went to work in the 1982 harvest. The flagship 865 had 15% more power and capacity than the 765 it replaced

MF 855

This model came with options of 14ft and 16ft Quick Attach headers, in New Profile or Power Flow versions.

This 855 dates from around 1983, however it has Dronningborg Power Flow header which was taken from another combine. (These Dronningborg headers were not available until 1985). From 1985, tables for Canadian built combines sold in Europe were built by Dronningborg in Denmark. These were either Free Flo (Non Power Flow) or were Power Flow tables. French built and Danish built tables were of different designs. The French built non Power Flow tables were known as New Profile. The Power Flow

uses a belt between the knife and intake auger, to feed the crop to the elevator. It is cutting oats at Great Porthamel Farm, Talgarth near Brecon where brothers Garry and Paul Jones have used the larger higher output Massey combines for twenty years, beginning with a 750. This 855 replaced a 760, it was a smaller combine with a 50in wide drum compared to the larger 60in width drum of the 760. It has the MF 800 series cab, which was one of the most extravagant on the market at the time of manufacture. The 855 was first launched in 1981, it is a six straw walker combine with a 5000 litre grain tank, and powered by a Perkins AT6 158hp. It has features such as the MF

'Cascade Separator' secondary separation system which was designed to allow a higher crop throughput over the walkers, retrieving grain losses. This comprised a three position rotor, and grain pan. An auger takes the retrieved grain to the left side of the combine, and an elevator takes the grain up to the pan under the walkers . There is a short auger at the top of the elevator to deliver the grain to the grain pan under the walkers. A 'High Inertia' Cylinder with eight heavy steel rasp bars and cast iron spiders to smooth out peak loads, was standard as well as the standard cab with RDS 2 channel performance monitor.

MF 865

Also a six straw walker combine, it has a larger sieve area and larger grain tank capacity of 6400 litres than the 855. This 1986 combine has spent all its life in the Herefordshire district until it came to the Talgarth area to work alongside the 855. This one has an 18ft Power Flow header, made by Massey Ferguson rather than Dronningborg and is powered by a Perkins AV8 184hp engine. Header options were 16ft, 18ft and 20ft. There were some differences between the Dronningborg and Marquette built Power Flow headers, the main one being that a separate pump for the reel drive was placed below the variable speed pulley on the combine, while on the French built ones, the pump for the reel drive was on the header itself a the back, as for the 625 series.

The Dronningborg headers had a sixth paddle on them on the intake auger, while the standard five paddle elevator was used before this on the Marquette built headers.

RETHRESHER

MF was the first manufacturer to use this system, introduced on the 400 and 500, and later used in a similar way by NH. A separate threshing system with a rasp bar rethresher, a mini drum and concave deal with unthreshed returns material which falls through the rear wider part of the sieve to the returns auger. From there, it is rethreshed, the re threshed material falls onto the end of the main grain pan and then onto the sieves, before it goes into the clean grain auger, rather than into the returns auger, so avoiding an additional load on the main cylinder. After rethreshing, the grain now it is rethreshed falls through the sieves into the returns auger.

— LEFT
MH 865 at Great Porthamel Farm Talgarth in Brecon Beacons.

CASCADE SEPARATOR

A secondary separation system similar to Multi Flow, where the grain coming off the walkers was combed out in a unit situated under the rear hood of the combine, before passing in the cross auger to the pan under the straw walkers. The rotor is situated higher up in the rear hood than the earlier Multi Flow system, making it less liable to block, which often arose with the Multi Flow. When the combine stopped, straw building up on the straw walkers would wrap round the rotor causing it to block.

POWERFLOW HEADER

Originally built at Kilmarnock, Power Flow headers were continued at Marquette. When combine production ceased at Marquette, Dronningborg made headers for the North American built combines sold in Europe, at the same time as they built the smaller MF combines, the 24 to 31 series. Headers for the North American built combines sold in the USA were made at Brantford. Dronningborg Power Flow headers differed from the Marquette built version in that they were lighter built and the angle of the rubber belts in relation to the bed were at a shallower angle. Dronningborg header only had a two speed power flow belt, and a single speed auger, whereas the Marquette header had a four speed belt, and a two speed auger with coarser built knife fingers, but otherwise it was a better built header than the Marquette version.

MF 865

This one was abandoned five years ago, when a contractor took over the combining. It used to cut 200 acres. It has now been sold and dismantled, and the engine and parts used to repair and keep another 865 over in Norfolk. The last year 865's were built in 1987. It is interesting to note that the last two years the combine were built, the unloading augers were red and the grain tank tops were red, prior to this from 1979, both the 855 and 865 had silver cabs and silver unloading augers and silver grain tank tops and the wheels were silver. Prior to 1979, the wheels were yellow, and the cab red with a white roof.

— FAR RIGHT

Rob White And Charlie Norman And 865.

— RIGHT AND TOP

Robbed of all her parts - Many parts have been salvaged to keep three combines run by Kevin and Stephen Clark in Norfolk running for several years to come.

MF 31XP

A product of the Dronningborg factory, the 31 and 31XP were made in the 1980's, and were sold alongside the 24, 27 and 29XP and the largest of the range, the 38.

This 31XP has a 16ft Free Flow header and is cutting oats at Talgarth Brecon. These were available with a Power flow or Free flow Quick Attach table in 10ft, 16ft or 18ft widths. It is a five straw walker combine, powered by a Perkins ATC63544 6 Cylinder 170hp engine. XP denotes an upgrade from the 31, with a larger engine. This model has an integrated cab with tinted glass, no corner pillar or steering column. On these models, the drivers platform is centrally placed, rather than offset to the left as on earlier MF combines. Straw chopper and spreaders and Yield Meters were options. Daniavision with printer, the computer in the cab, which enabled all machine settings to be undertaken electronically and machine functions monitored was available on the largest model 38. An MF 31 was priced at £63,000 in October 1987.

MF 36

This MF 36 and MF 40 are cutting grass seed at Bowling Green Farm, near Hereford, Herefordshire, with Shelbourne Reynolds header attachments for grass seed. These models were sold in the 30/40 Series starting from the 30 up to the largest, the 40. Manufactured at the time of the AGCO take over of MF, the 36 was offered with cutting widths of 14ft, 16ft or 18ft, it was sold with options of Free Flow or Power flow headers but here is using a Shelbourne Reynolds grass seed attachment. The 36 features the MF High Inertia drum, Rotary Separator which is standard on the 36 and 40, and has a 6400 litre grain tank. It is a five straw walker machine and is powered by a Valmet 220hp 6 cylinder diesel engine. The Datavision II, MF's monitoring, control and information system was redesigned to give more information and was standard on this range. The Field Star Precision Farming System for yield mapping for which MF had a Gold Medal in 1996, was an option.

— **RIGHT**
MF 36 and 40 together in grass seed.

MF 40

Working alongside the 36 cutting grass seed in Herefordshire, the 40 was the largest in the range, sold in the 1990's. As at 1997 specifications the header was offered with options of 18ft, 20ft and 22ft. Powered by a 6 cylinder Valmet 612 DSJL 300hp engine, the grain tank held 7900 litres and had the benefit of the standard Rotary Separator situated behind the main drum, this with the additional grate and concave under the separator aided separation of heavier crops in damp conditions before the straw passes to the walkers. The AL Auto Level options became available on this range. Straw choppers were standard but spreaders were offered as an option.

The 30/40 range was phased out with the introduction of the 7000 series in 2000.

— **TOP**
MF 40 just finished a field of barley. The machine belongs to Duncan Cameron of Letton Court, Letton, Hereford.

MF 7276

By 2000, the 30/40 series was replaced by the 7200 series which were launched from Dronningorg's Randers factory, including the 7276, the largest in a series of seven from 7250, 7252 to 7274 and 7276, from 165hp to 325hp. Some were in AL hillside versions. These were once the largest combines on offer from MF.

The 7276 below is cutting oilseed rape near Bridgnorth in Shropshire. This combine cuts in the region of 1200 acres a season for a contractor.

They featured the standard Autoglide Automatic table control system, the Power Flow table unique to MF was standard, with the Freeflow table an option, green emission compliant engines made by Valmet of Finland, with optional rotary separator. Precision farming systems appeared in the form of MF Fieldstar for yield monitoring and mapping.

ACTIVA

One of 7200 Activa series line up for 2010, this one fits in between the smallest 7240 and largest 7247, The 7245 is available in an S and S-AL version. This one is an S-AL version with higher output, the AL denotes Auto Level version. The AL system levels the combine rump across slopes by pivoting the final front drives, allowing the combine to work across slopes of 20 per cent.

It has a Free Flow header, cutting width options are from 4.20m to 7.60m, and retains the MF High Inertia threshing drum, together with a more recent feature unique to MF. the Power Feed Roller PFR. This model also has the PFR Plus, a system which improves crop transfer between the header and the elevator by distributing the crop over the full width of the elevator housing.

It also has the MCS Multi Crop Separator - a Rotary Separator fitted behind the beater to give centrifugal separation to the grain and agitate the straw as it passes over the walkers, as well as the Plus which allows the concave to be removed completely for added grain separation in wet conditions or high yielding crops. Powered by an Iveco NEF 243hp engine, the grain tank holds 7000 litres.

— **ABOVE**
ACTIVA at LAMMA show.
— **BELOW**
7245S-AL at the cereals event.

MF BETA 7260-AL4

The Beta models for 2010 comprise the 7260 and 7270, with AL versions in each, ranging in hp from 275 to 335.

This 7260 AL4 is a four wheel drive combine, it is working near Leominster, Herefordshire at Lawtonbury Farm and belongs to Mr. William of Lyke. Larger than the Activa model, it is powered by the latest generation Tier III an AGCO Sisu/74ETA 275hp engine, cuttings widths are available from 4.80m to 6.60m. The Power flow table is available as an option with Free Flow fitted as standard. The unique Power Feed Roller in front of the main intake elevator is featured on this model, as well as the well known MF Rotary Separator with the MCS Plus, which has a concave that can be rotated up over the top of the Rotary Separator when it is not required and High Inertia Cylinder. A five straw walker combine, the grain tank can hold 8200 litres.

This combine is an Auto Level, allowing the combine to work across slopes up to 20% and also it can level up and down slopes of up to 4%. It also has 4WD, a powered rear axle fitted as standard on AL models, which gives better steering control and traction on slopes. It has a more luxurious XLR Cab than the smaller Activa, with automatic air conditioning, 3D adjustable steering column and Agritronic plus monitor system.

CENTORA 7280 AL

The Centora range for 2010 consists of the 7280 and 7282 with AL versions, The 7280 is powered by an AGCO SISU Power 8.4 378hp engine, and is an eight straw walker machine, threshing is undertaken with a high inertia 600mm cylinder and rotary separator, and it is offered with header widths of 20ft to 30ft, with PowerFlow and AutoLevel headers. The grain tank holds 9500 litres. The Min Till straw chopper with eight rows of serrated blades is standard with optional straw chopper. The Hi Stream grain management cleaning system with two cascade steps with air blasts from the fans and separate re-thresher is designed to handle up to 100 tonnes an hour. The luxury cab has tinted glass, air suspension seat, and 3D tilt steering column, and is equipped with Datavision for all machine monitoring and adjustments. List price for 2010 with 7.6m powerflow header is £264,704.

9280 DELTA

Launched at Agritechnica for the 2010 harvest, the 9280 Delta features conventional threshing with twin rotor separation. The main feature of this combine is that it is powered by a 7 cylinder AGCO SISU 9.8 litre 496hp engine. According to the manufacturer, it is the first on the market and in its class using Selective Catalytic Reduction Technology, (SCR) a system for engine management and exhaust-gas treatment. SCR technology injects AdBlue into the exhaust system, optimising combustion, neutralizing nitrogen oxides and reducing particulate matter. It helps the environment and allows for optimal engine performance and fuel efficiency.

It retains the MF proven High Inertia cylinder, which is 600mm diameter. A rotor feeder behind the cylinder splits the crop where it is forced into the Hi-separation rotors.

A new feature is a unique Loading Bay in a wide inlet area from the Rotor Feeder, which allows for maximum entry and smooth transition of the crop to be passed through to the two Hi-Separation rotors with spiral formation separation tines to assist crop movement, which MF call the HyPerforma Threshing Technology. Rotor speed is electronically adjustable.

The other main feature is the Venturi Cleaning System, a two step system pressurized, so an optimized airflow across 100% of the sieves surface is maintained. The aerodynamically designed air inlets situated in the middle of the fan housing create a "venture" effect raising the amount of air for efficient grain cleaning required for the higher grain output from the HyPerforma system.

It has a Separate Re thresher and the grain tank has a capacity of 10,500 litres 9500 for AL version.

The integral cab has the MF DATAVISION II with all the extra comforts such as air sprung seat, heating, air conditioning. A High Speed Minimal tillage Chopper and chaff spreader is standard. It is also available as an AL version.

It is available in header sizes from 6.8m to 9.2m.

And one which never came.

MF 1 TRACTOR DRAWN WHOLE CROP HEADER

This prototype belongs to farmer and vintage enthusiast Andrew Rogers at Sollars Hope, Ross-on-Wye, Herefordshire, and was purchased from H J Pugh's collectors sale at Ledbury. They were made in the late 1980's and early 1990's, and it is thought only a few were made and those were sent abroad. According to a brochure dating from 1991, it required a tractor with a lift capacity of approximately 1400kg. It has a 2 metre table, and being within the width of the tractor, it was ideal for narrow lanes. It was designed by MF as a whole crop harvester for use where broken straw is useful as an animal feed. It cuts, gathers and threshes the crop as in a conventional combine, but instead of the straw being disposed on the ground behind the combine, it is finely broken and either collected in bags or blown into a trailer. The whole crop harvester could also be used for stationery threshing. The grain was collected in separate bags. Few if any of these were sold.

JOHN DEERE

JOHN DEERE 630

John Deere combines have been imported into the UK since 1958. The 530 and 630 combines were in the company's product line up at the beginning of 1966, when John Deere Limited first started trading in the UK and Ireland from Langar

Made at Zweibrucken Germany, they were designed for the long straw crops of Europe, and some came to Britain. They were based on a widened and updated version of the classic John Deere 55 built in North America in the 1940's and 1950's, which has been followed on all German built series to date. The first of the 30 series were built at Manheim, production was transferred to Zweibrucken in the 1960's, the 630 was the first to be built there. The 630 had a 100hp Perkins diesel engine, four walkers, a 90 bushel grain tank, and 41in cylinder. It was offered with 10ft to 14ft headers. Announced in 1965, it was the fourth of a series from 330,

with a later two models, the 730 and a pto version of the 330. This series remained in production until replaced by the 900 series in 1972.

JOHN DEERE 952

In 1978, the economical 952 was added to the 900 range for the following harvest, with four straw walkers but there was no cross shaker on this model. Two new concepts came with the 900 series, the Cross Shaker and an optional revermatic transmission which allowed the operator to change gear by pushing the clutch pedal half way, but it reversed the combines direction if pushed the full distance. Quik-Tatch headers also came with these models, and option of hydraulic reel fore and aft adjustment. In 1958, all John Deere machines followed the tractor lead and were John Deere green with yellow wheels, and lettering. Reels on combines at this time were yellow and cabs were an option.

— **BELOW**

The combine below belongs to Glyn Bemand, The Woodings, Bromyard and still cuts some barley and oats this stock farm. Powered by a John Deere diesel 4 cylinder 85hp engine it was four straw walker combine, offered with cutting widths of 10, 12 and 14ft, and had a grain tank capacity of 2180 litres. It was sold alongside the 955 to 975, and 965H. The 5's were an upgrade on the first 900 series introduced in 1972.

JOHN DEERE 985

Later in 1978, Zweibrucken announced their largest combine to date, the 985. This was upgraded later in 1981, with the 10 series. Offered with cutting widths of 14, 16 and 18ft, it is a six straw walker combine, powered by a John Deere 6 cylinder 170hp engine. The Cross Shaker system which consisted of 6 sets of oscillating rotating tines above the walkers was standard. Revermatic and straw chopper were offered as options, and there was a Hydro 4, hydrostatic option, offered later on this model. A cab with air conditioning was offered as an option for this model.

— Right

This 1982 985 with a 14ft cut, still serves contractor Will Sayce well, it is seen working near Wormlow, Ross-on-Wye, Herefordshire, and cuts in the region of three hundred acres. It was the top of the range combine of the 900 series, and the largest combine John Deere made at this time for the UK market, it has manual transmission and the JD Cross Shaker system.

JD 1052

This model was available with 10, 12 and 14ft headers, it is a four straw walker combine, powered by a John Deere 85hp 4 cylinder, turbo charged diesel engine. It has a SG2 John Deere cab and a straw chopper was an option, with a grain tank capacity of 3000 litres, with hydrostatic steering. The yellow reel of the 900 series changed to black on this series.

— LEFT

This 1055 was normally sold with the standard header, but here has the 812 series cutting platform, which has a larger intake auger and is heavier built. It is cutting winter barley at Snodhill, near Dorstone, Herefordshire. Available with choice of four cutting widths from 10, to 16ft, this 1055 has the 812 series John Deere platform. It is a four straw walker combine with the Cross Shaker system above the straw walkers, and is powered by a John Deere 6 cylinder 105hp diesel engine.

Announced later in 1981, the 10 series consisted of the 1052, up to the 1085 and 2085 Hydro-4 with the 1055 and 1065 being middle of the range. The 10 series used the 200 series headers and the SG2 Sound Gard cabs made at Bruchsal, Germany were available, and introduced in 1983.

JD 1065

This four straw walker model has the SG2 Cab with air conditioning, it has a Standard 12ft Quik Tatch header, other headers available were 10, 14 and 16ft. A nitrogen-charged accumulator incorporated into the hydraulic circuit, maintains header height over uneven fields. Powered by a John Deere Turbo charged diesel 6 cylinder 125hp engine, it had a 4300 litre grain tank. There were monitors for shaft speeds, grain losses. The transmission was manual rather than hydrostatic, which featured the JD Posi Torque variable drive, which maintains the right propulsion belt tension in all conditions. The Posi Torque ground drive transfers engine power through a variable speed control to the 4 speed transmission and front drive wheels. Steering was hydrostatic. This 1065 is seen here working in the Golden Valley area of Herefordshire, cutting winter barley.

JD 1177

The 1100 series was a major change in Europe for JD combines, beginning with the 1188 in 1987 for the following harvest. The series had many improvements in visibility and control for the operator. As on other manufacturers combines, the lengthened feeder house now had a reverser to remove cutter bar jams easily.

The 800 series grain platforms were introduced at the same time. These had attachments for rape and sunflowers and were a heavier built header, built around a computer designed, robust frame with an option of built in dividers. There were 900 headers available which had a flexible platform. With additions in 1989, the 13 model line up included the 1133, to 1177 with a Hydro-4 option and 1188 with Hydro-4 options. Most were built at Zweibrucken and the engines were built at Saran France. Harvest Trak Monitor was available situated on the can corner post, as an option, which monitored grain losses.

A later 1170 model made at Horizontina Brazil, was available to compliment the 2200 series models launched for the 1997 season. The later 1175 was also made in Brazil and became the 1450 CWS combine

— **Below**

This 1177 has an 800 series header and still works on a stock and mixed farm near Hay-on-Wye, Herefordshire. A five straw walker combine with five Cross Shaker units, it is powered by a John Deere 6 cylinder Turbo charged 150hp engine, it features the Quik Tatch system and was offered with header widths of 12 to 18ft, with header reverser. A few more automatic header controls were now available as standard on this series. Pre Selection of header height was on the Master control lever which also controlled ground speed, with a header height resume button which returns the header to a preselected cutting height, hydraulic fore and aft and height control, as well as electric reel speed control. Transmission was by means of the John Deere Posi Torque ground drive system, on this model with mechanical transmission, which also has a straw chopper which is put out of work by a simple baffle inside the hood. The cleaning system has a scroll type fan and the Slope Master cleaning shoe, which work together to give more performance on slopes. The 1177 had green grain top extensions instead of the previous black extensions.

The curved windshield sloped to the rear and the unloading auger swung forward 110 degrees.

— **Bottom**

Small 800 series header. Note the spare crop lifters hanging on the header at the back.

The 1100 SII series introduced in 1990 for the following harvest superceded the 1100 series, and were the largest three

models in a range from the existing 1175, 1166 S11 to 1188 S11 Hydro 4.with increased capacity and engine power, an on board computer and four wheel drive option, with an improved optional straw choppers.

JD 2054

These were known as the Z Series 660mm Twin cylinder combines and were launched in 1993. This one was the smallest in a range of five models, from 2054 to 2066. The main features were the introduction of the Hillmaster slope levelling system, and a Techcentre cab with a passenger seat offering more space and comfort for the operator. There were more automatic adjustments such as pre selected cylinder speed settings, concave clearance and fan speed.

A new advanced design of threshing system appeared, the Dual-Flow high capacity cleaning system, with high velocity turbine fans being used, including a pre cleaning stage where heavy chaff is removed before the grain reaches the chaffer and sieve.

— LEFT

The 2054 five straw walker model was offered with cutting widths from 4.25 to 5.50metres. The one here has an 816 header, and is cutting oilseed rape in Herefordshire. There were more Automatic header functions, including pre set cutting height on the Master Control joy stick, Auto Float function which allows the header to follow ground contours for lodged crops, Auto Reel where the reel speed changes automatically with the ground speed. There was also Auto Combine Adjustment for changing crops, cylinder, concave and fan speed.

Powered by a John Deere 6 cylinder 180hp turbo charged engine, it had hydrostatic transmission and steering and a grain tank capacity of 6000 litres.

— LEFT

2056 cutting barley, this is also a five straw walker combine with the 800 series 8-16 header, and was a slightly larger model to the 2054, with an engine of 205hp, and grain tank capacity of 6500 litres. As on the smaller model, it has hydrostatic transmission, and retains the John Deere Cross Shaker system, the cylinder size is the same, the diameter being 66cm, with twin cylinder system. It was offered with cuttings widths of 4.25m to 5.50m, and again featured the Auto Combine Adjustments.

22 SERIES

Introduced for the 1997 season, these 2200 Series models in the Z Series replaced the 2000 Series models and had higher horsepower engines and improved transmissions. The 22 Series retained the Twin Cylinder system used in the 20 series, with a large main drum followed by a smaller secondary drum, and a new hydrostatic ground drive was featured on the larger 2258, 2264 and 2266 models. The Tech Centre cab was retained but with increased technology- a new dual screen monitor which showed the walker and cleaning shoe performance simultaneously and a foot operated switch for the unloading auger. Contour Master was introduced as an option, which featured fully automatic header height control as well as lateral tilt and ground contact strips under the header which allow the header to automatically adjust to the ground contours on the move.

Other features used on the 20 series were retained, the Dual Flow system with the pre cleaner to remove chaff and debris before material enters the chaffer and sieve, and Auto combine adjustments for fan speed, cylinder speed, and concave openings for 9 different crops. Headers sizes were from 4.2m, to 7m widths.

2254

This 2254 is one of a fleet of John Deere combines run by contractors A Legge and Sons and is working near Bromyard Herefordshire cutting wheat. It has the 800 series 8-16 16ft header. The engines of this series exceeded tighter emission regulations which were likely to become standard from 1998. It was offered with headers from 4.25m to 5.50m. Powered by a John Deere 180hp 6 cylinder engine, it was a five straw walker machine with 6000 litre grain tank capacity, and was offered with an optional straw chopper and chaff spreader. It was the smallest in a five model range up to the flagship 2266. This model has a straw chopper folded up out of operation.

9660WTS HILLMASTER11

This was one of six models, 9540, 9560, 9580, 9640, 9660 and 9680 with engine power from 200hp to 310hp, featuring a new WTS System. Threshing is with a single drum system with 600mm cylinder and a beater with separation carried out by a new 11 step straw walker design and an overhead agitator tine drum, the Power Separator. This model also used the new 600R Platforms, available from 4.30m to 9.15m. These were heavier in design, with an 80hp header reverser, which takes power directly from the engine, epicylic knife drive to an in line knife motion with vibration free operation and larger 600mm intake auger. An electro hydraulic multi coupler combines all hydraulic hoses and electric connections with a single point attachment.

This series also featured a Power Separator drum with retractable fingers above the straw walkers to aid separation, and a Duo Flo cleaning system, the four fans with scroll type rotors accelerate air more than the paddle type blades. A new Quadra-Flo Cleaning system was introduced which has heavy duty augers with a Pre Cleaner, chaffer sieve and four independent Dual Flo rotors. More technology appeared, Automatic Combine Adjustments for concave, cleaning fan speeds, cylinder, and recommended chaffer and sieve adjustments are indicated, Header Trak display for automatic header height control, Vision Trak display for monitoring the cleaning shoe and separator.

The models were available as a Hillmaster option.

1450 CWS

The five straw walker 1450 and six walker 1550 Series 2, previously known as CWS, (Cylinder Walker Separation) are the smallest models which took over from the 1170, 1177 and 1188 models), and are made in Horizontina in Brazil. This is John Deere's newest combine factory which opened in 1989. These models have 6000 to 6800 litre grain tanks and 204hp and 262hp JD Turbocharged engines respectively, are used with the 600R platforms or the updated 300R series. The most basic of the models, they lack the sophisticated electronics of the other models but they feature proven John Deere Cylinder Walker Separation, with the optional Power Separator which aids separation towards the rear of the walkers. Cleaning is with the eccentric 8 blade fan and reciprocating chaffer and sieve and standard Slopemaster cleaning shoe which cuts grain losses on slopes.

— **LEFT**

1450 CWS in dealers yard, Alexander and Duncan, Leominster, Hereford. It is a five straw walker model, and has a 616 header 16 ft. Powered by a 6068H 191hp engine, the grain tank holds 6800 litres with the extension, and the drum is 610mm diameter. It was offered with 614R 14ft to 622R 22ft headers. The Power Separator above the straw walkers was an option on this model. The combine came with a standard straw chopper and the Slope Master cleaning shoe, but chaff spreader was optional. It is now updated to CWS Series Two.

— **LEFT**

This 9660WTS Hillmaster II is seen working near Weobley Herefordshire, cutting Oilseed rape between the storms during the difficult unsettled harvest of 2008. Powered by a John Deere Power Tech 302hp 6 cylinder engine, it is a 6 straw walker machine with grain tank capacity of 9000 litres.

Hillmaster is available on all S, C, T and W Series models.

The Hillmaster II has automatic levelling that recognises a change in slope, this automatically oscillates the entire combine body up to 15% to compensate, in combination with the Slope Master system, which maintains level land capacity on slopes up to 7%. The Hillmaster is able to harvest on slopes up to 22% with no losses in performance. This is the automatic side hill model, with a whole body compensation system for hillside work, rather than just the wheels. The separator and sieves-cleaning shoe remain level, as distinct from other manufacturers which use a cleaning shoe levelling system. The grain tank stays level giving better weight distribution and greater traction because the weight is distributed more evenly on the tyres.

The front plate of the feeder house allows the header to follow ground contours. Two heavy duty cylinders are integrated into the combine side frames. As the cylinders extend or retract, they move the final drives and wheels up or down to keep the combine body level. A control box is attached to the combine frame on the left side of the machine. An electronic tilt sensor changes in slope and sends an electrical signal to the solenoid valve. The solenoid then extends or retracts the proper cylinder.

T SERIES

The T Series was launched in 2008 along with the W C and S Series combines. The T560 is one of four models, T550, T660 and T670.They are five and six straw walker machines with engine power from 290hp to 400hp. They are all available as an i model.

Models feature the Multi Drum Separation system. The T Series uses a 660mm cylinder with 10 rasp bars and concave and beater for threshing, a stripper roller for separation and overshot beater and tangentially mounted tine separator drum with a large wrap concave, situated behind the cylinder, and six walkers.

The 'T' Series design comes from two previous combines plus the new concept of the Tangential tine cylinder. The success of this combine is due to the crop flow which goes over the first overshot rear beater rather than under it, the crop then flows under the second Tangential 'T' tine cylinder and then under a conventional beater behind this. The first stripper drum roller and beater came from the C series models, the T rotor and beater were new to the T series, from where its name comes from. The rear beater and grate under it came from the W Series combine.

The Quadro Flo cleaning System was originally developed for the 9000 Series and uses a heavy duty auger type preparation system, pre cleaner, chaffer sieve and 4 Duo fan rotors, from which high velocity air moves through the pre cleaner to lift the chaff and dirt away, before the material reaches the chaffer and sieve. John Deere is the only company to use an auger system, the heavy duty conveyor augers are used instead of a preparation pan, which gives reduced slope sensitivity and self cleaning.

The T Series also features ACA Auto Combine Adjustment, which adjusts cylinder speed, cleaning fan speed, concave clearance main chaffer pre cleaner and sieve openings in any one of 16 factory set crop settings, including a remote cleaning shoe adjustment where all 6 elements of the pre cleaner and sieves are connected directly to a dedicated activator.

The T series are offered as Hillmaster versions, as on the 9000 Series.

The 600R Series headers from widths of 14ft to 30ft are offered with these models. Features include an 80hp header reverse, direct from the engine, auto reel reverse, and a single point attachment of electrical and hydraulic lines.

The 600R Series headers have a 600mm reel auger, the same diameter as the threshing drum. The platform also uses a linear knife drive for increased reliability and performance. The reel bars have single tines instead of twin tines for cost efficient servicing. John Deere is at present the only company to use single point latching for the header connections, this system allows the header to be latched and all hydraulic and electrical connections to be made in one go. The longer feeder housing from the header intake to the drum is a noticeable feature of John Deere combines.

For Residual Management, the Standard straw chopper spreads a uniform layer of straw and chaff together. There are also options of a Twin disc chaff spreader, which allows deflectors to be adjusted to allow for side winds, so that chaff can be spread over the full header width. The Optional Premium chopper allows chaff and straw to be windrowed together or spread chaff while windrowing the straw.

There is sophisticated technology available on the T Series. Harvest Doc is offered as an option with this series, which automatically collects all harvesting data, yields, moisture for later documentation and analysis.

Green Star is an option, for more accurate operation, which allows manual or fully automatic steering to levels of accuracy up to 2, 10 or 30 cms.

T560

This T560 during its first harvest is cutting winter barleyfor Will Davies of Upper Court Farm, near Hay-on-Wye' Herefordshire. It is a five straw walker combine powered by a 6 cylinder Power Tech turbo charged 350hp engine with 100,00 litre grain tank. It is offered with the 600 R Series headers in cutting widths from 4.30m to 9.15m.

T560I

All T models are available also as an 'i' combine with JD Performance options- Autotrac Assisted steering, Harvest Smart Auto Feed rate Control which adjusts ground speed until full capacity is reached or loss limit are reached and Harvest Doc collects harvest data yields, moisture etc for later analysis Ag Management Solutions.

All T Series except the smallest T550, as well as other John Deere combines excepting the W Series, are offered with the Pro Drive option. This is the latest advance in transmission drive technology, and is an automatic-shift transmission, which eliminates the need to constantly monitor and adjust the hydrostatic control lever or stop to shift gears while harvesting. Pro Drive enables the driver to change between two speed ranges with the push of a button a normal harvesting speed can be set and then a further faster speed for transport or faster field work. There is also an integrated differential lock.

This demonstration model of the five straw walker T560i from Alexander and Duncan, John Deere dealers of Leominster is working in OSR near Weobley, Herefordshire, in the difficult harvesting conditions of 2008. Powered by a John Deere 350hp Power tech 6 cylinder turbocharged engine, it has a grain tank capacity of 10,000 litres and the fuel tank holds 800 litres. The T Series is manufactured at Zweibrucken, all John Deere combines for the European market have been made at Zweibrucken since 1965, apart from exceptions such as the STS. This model differs from the T560 in that it has all the 'i' Intelligent features: Harvest Smart, Autotrac and Harvest Doc. Cost of a C560i for the 2010 harvest is £288,940 with 9.15 header.

C 670I

This new C670i had recently arrived from the factory at Zweibrucken, and here is on a test track at Langar Nottinghamshire, the UK John Deere Headquarters, where it can be test driven by Trainee Technicians. This is the top of the range of the Series complete with all the 'i' Systems. Powered by a JD 6 cylinder 400hp engine, the grain tank holds 10,000 litres it has the full range of performance enhancements such as Auto Trac and Harvest Smart. The cab is also equipped with modern ATC-Automatic Climate Control.

C670 HILLMASTER

This model with 600 R 25ft header belongs to contractor John Derricut and is working in the Bridgnorth district in Shropshire, cutting oats. Powered by a JD 6 cylinder 9 litre 400hp power Tech Plus engine, it has a 10,000 litre grain tank. The Premium Straw chopper with 88 rotating knives and 57 stationery knives are standard. It is swathing the straw here, it has an integrated straw chopper and chaff spreader, for chopping, the deflector plates are altered to channel the straw though the chopper. The 600 R headers can be switched between any of the John Deere W, T, C and S series combines. This one is also a Hillmaster model, the cab remains level. It uses a 3 speed Pro Drive transmission, which shifts between two ranges for precise speed control.

S690I

The S690i, formerly the STS, is the highest capacity combine produced by the company and features a revolutionary Single Tine Separation. Since the launch of the STS 9880 model in 2001 for the 2002 season, it has been built at the Harvester Works at East Moline Illinois USA.

Based on two variants of the S series, one of which was the 9750 STS -only marketed in the US, which was launched in 1999, the S690i was designed for the European market.

It consists of a single high performance rotor in a cage to expand the crop as it progresses to the rear, giving a high crop flow and capacity and good separation.

There are three stages to the Separation rotor, the first part consists of an auger with three flights. The rifling grooves on the bullet-shaped rotor move large volumes of crop through the rotor. The second part contains the threshing elements with a concave underneath, here the crop is propelled rearwards from the threshing section to the separation section by the heavy duty vanes on the top cover. The third part of the separator has six rows of tines angled to comb and penetrate the crop mat, freeing any remaining grain. Here are the cast modular iron separation grids with removable sections underneath.

At the time was the largest JD combine with a 325hp engine and 300 bushel grain tank capacity.

Today, the upgraded and latest S690i is made at Harvester Works at East Moline Illinois USA and currently the S690i is the largest whole body levelling combine in the world. It is also available as a Hillmaster version.

— LEFT

This S690i , belonging to a contractor Chris Prinold from Telford, is cutting wheat near Shrewsbury, Shropshire. Powered by a Tier III Power Tech JD 6 Cylinder 530hp engine, its fuel tank can hold 1155 litres and grain tank has a capacity of 11,000 litres. It cuts around 2000 to 2500 acres annually. The Dyna Flo 11 cleaning system it uses was designed for the S690i which gives a high volume cleaning system. The 'i' intelligence enhancement features are standard on S690i combines. The combine is offered with optional 4 wheel drive heavy duty axle. These have become more popular since the two successive wet harvests of 2007 and 2008. The combine here has a 30ft Biso VX 900 Cropranger header, which is an all in one header. For OSR the side knives fold out, and the header can be extended an additional 70cm from the cab, without adding extra filler plates and other parts. The Premium straw chopping system is standard on the S690i.

S690I

S Series

The S690i, formerly the STS, is the highest capacity combine produced by the company. The revolutionary Single Tine Separation is a patented John Deere technology. Since the launch of this model in 2001 for the 2002 season, it has been made at the Harvester Works at East Moline Illinois USA, and is the only model made there.

With an 11,000 litre grain tank, it is the highest capacity JD model on the market. The STS uses a single rotor and externally looks much like the US equivalent but inside it is very different to the American version due to the differences in climate and crops. The European version has a higher horsepower engine to cope with the higher yielding crops and straw found in Europe, and a faster knife drive, while the US models have a less vigorous threshing system due to the lighter crops there. Both S series versions are made in the US rather than Zweibricken, The 530hp S690i is the largest whole body levelling combine on the market.

The S series along with all JD combines also has a longer feeder house set a lower angle and further forward giving better visibility. The rotary system used in the S series is a different concept to other rotary models on the market in that it has an innovative high performance rotor which increases the separator capacity. The crop

flows from the feed accelerator directly to the stepped rotor via the auger feed section of the rotor, which grabs the crop as it spins. This allows the crop mat to expand as it moves through the separator. It's tine combing action, combined with pull and release expansion, helps free grain trapped in the crop mat, resulting in significant grain saving and efficient use of horsepower. The rotor has six rows of tines which are set at an angle to aid penetration of the crop mat, so freeing any

remaining grain. The Dyna Flo cleaning system was developed specifically to match the high output of this combine, giving high volume cleaning coupled to electronic in cab adjustments of sieve settings. The Dyna Flow scroll type fan blows a high volume of air across the cleaning shoe.

Available only as a 'i' series, the S690i's have all the intelligent integrated features of Harvest Smart, AutoTrac and Harvest Doc on board together with Greenstar 2

Guidance system, which allows a choice between manual and fully automatic steering to an accuracy of 2, 10 or 30 cm. It is powered by the 13.5 litre 530hp John Deere Power Tech engine. List price of a 690i with 9.15 header for the 2010 harvest was £340,513 with a 9.15m header.

The S Series is the only combine with a folding unloading auger.

NEW HOLLAND

CLAEYS M80

Produced from 1958 to 1967, it was sold alongside the M103 and M140, during which time the Claeys name changed to Clayson in 1953. Claeys claimed it had an output of 4½ tons an hour. It was known as the New Holland Clayson M80. It was replaced by the M89 and larger M133/M135 models. A modern combine for its time, it had hydraulic reel and table lift, a drum speed variator, and a speed regulator for the pick-up reel, as well as ground speed variator which gave unbroken range of ground speeds with an infinite range of rations between gears.

This M80 is seen working in barley near Pembridge, Kington, Herefordshire, where it has been on the same farm since new. It was purchased by the Edwards family of Stocklow Manor Farm in 1963, and is still going strong, after a break of a few years. A four straw walker model, it has an 8ft 3in header, and 18in diameter drum, with 42 bushel or 1500 litre grain tank, and is powered by a 55hp Fordson industrial diesel engine, although the M80 was also available with an air cooled Deutz diesel engine.

CLAEYS M103

This combine was a success all over the world and the only model referring to a feature, the inside dimensions of the frame were 103cm. Manufactured by Werkhuizen Leon Claeys Zedelgem Belgium, it was introduced in 1958 until 1966, 27,500 units were built. It was introduced in Britain at the 1959 Smithfield Show, it succeeded the MZ combine, and was offered in widths of 8ft 3in, 10ft and 12ft, powered by an 80hp diesel engine, and was available as a tanker or bagger version. It was a straight through harvester, and had a direct drive transmission. The wheels were driven direct by the axles and not through belts or chains. In 1962, a smaller M103 was £2,395, and the 12ft machine was £2,415. It was marketed through Bamfords Ltd of Uttoxeter in Staffordshire. It weighed 9,867lb and was said to have an output of up to 6 tons an hour. A straw chopper and spreader were offered as options.

Over 40 years since the last one was made, they are still working here and there. One such example is this combine belonging to Mr David Jones and his son

Robert, of Chelmick Farm, Church Stretton Shropshire, seen here cutting oats. It is a four straw walker machine, with drum width of 41in and Diameter 24in. With over 50 harvests under its belt, this 10ft cut tanker version has a 55 bushel grain tank, and is powered by a Ford 6 cylinder engine. It is thought to date from the late 1950s and was cutting about 50 acres a year on this farm where it has been since 1978. The bagger versions had four bagging off outlets. It is now pensioned off but kept for preservation and used as a back up combine to a 1530.

— THIS PAGE

NH Clayson 1530 And M103 together. This New Holland Clayson 1520 joined the M103 two years ago at Chelmick Farm, Church Stretton. Here the two are cutting wheat.

NH CLAYSON 1530
Sperry New Holland

This replaced the M133, and production ran from 1971 to 1981 during which time the Company became Sperry Rand Belgium N.V in 1977, and two years later, Sperry N.V. and was marketed by Sperry Rand. It was one of the rugged built 1500 series sold during the 1970's, in between the 1520, 1540, 1545 and 1550. The first of the series the larger 1550 appeared in 1968. The 1530 was offered with a newly designed Quick attach header in cutting widths of 8ft 6in, to 13ft, with the reel speed adjusted on the go. There were additional operator controls from the cab, reel height could also be adjusted from the driver's seat and horizontal adjustment was mechanical or hydraulic. Powered by a Ford 6 cylinder 113hp engine, it featured the New Holland Constant - Flow Feed System, where a high initial threshing capacity was matched by efficient walkers and cleaning components. The constant flow was maintained for different crop

conditions, by altering the 42in diameter six tine bar reel for speed and position, and according to the sales literature, the crop flow was regulated into the threshing area to obtain maximum drum loading, and so threshing was kept at a continuous level ensuring a higher combine output. The reel was designed to slide on exclusive curved support arms. It was offered with options of tracks, a maize header and cab header trolley.

— ABOVE

Dating from 1978, this four straw walker 12ft cut 1530 is here cutting wheat at Chelmick Farm, Church Stretton, Shropshire. It bears the name New Holland Clayson, and was marketed by Sperry Rand. It had a Cab Craft cab added at a later date. The combine now cuts 50 acres a year since a M103 was retired in 2009. Steering was hydrostatic and the grain tank held 2400 litres or 66 galls.

NH CLAYSON 1545
Sperry New Holland

This was a large capacity combine in its day and featured the new header design and Constant Flow Feed System used on the 1530. Introduced in 1971 alongside the 1520, 1540 and 1580 it was available for about seven years, and fitted in the 1500 range between the 1520, 1540, 1540AL and 1550. It was offered with headers of 13, 15 and 17ft which were Quick Attach the header could be removed for transport in minutes without any tools and used the hydropneumatic header compensation to follow ground contours. The reel speed was adjusted by a mechanical variator. It had hydrostatic steering, and a hydraulically operated ground speed variator. Cabs were still not standard on combines, they were offered as an option, along with header trailer, tracks, different length unloading augers, crop lifters and different equipment for harvesting different crops, such as grass and rape seed.

— ABOVE

This 1545 dating from 1979, near the end of the production of this model, is a five straw walker machine with 13ft cut header, cuts about 25 acres annually on a stock rearing farm belonging to Alan Layghton of Stall Farm, near Vowchurch in Herefordshire. It once cut 100 acres and when new was a high capacity machine working on a large arable farm near Cirencester. It is cutting barley grown for animal feed. Powered by a Ford 6 cylinder 130hp engine, the grain tank holds 72 bushels, 2610 litres.

NH 8070

The 8000 Series was launched at the Royal Show in 1976, with the flagship 8080, marketed by the Sperry New Holland Division of Sperry Rand Ltd, of Aylesbury, Buckinghamshire. Described as a giant combine harvester, it was claimed by Sperry to be the largest available in terms of capacity in the UK at this time, and was available for the 1977 harvest. The 8080 was the first 5 walker combine to be built at Zedelgem. It was still available with an open driver's platform although most units had a cab. It featured a new operators cab, restyled with lower noise level of no more than 82 decibels, and made from an all-glass front, using a glass to glass jointing system, it did away with pillars. The 8080 was offered with the rigid strongly built New Holland headers in 13ft to 22ft cutting widths. There were new ideas in technical design, like an unique header-flotation system. This was hydro-pneumatic and connected to a sensitivity gauge in front of the operator which enables him to made adjustments to maintain adequate flotation. The 8000 series used the Rotary Separator, a special feature of New Holland combines, introduced on the 1550 which works on the principle of centrifugally separating the grain before discharging the straw on to the walkers. This was the same size as the main drum on the 8080. The crop is subjected to a sudden extra change of speed and direction with another drum and concave. Powered by a 6 cylinder 175hp Mercedes-Benz engine, the 8080 was a six walker machines. Ford and Fiat engines were also used in the 8000 series.

8070

This was the second of the 8000 series available a year after the 8080 in 1978, and was sold alongside the 1500 series and the 8080. The cab was at first an option but later standard on the 8070. Powered by a 6 cylinder 155hp direct injection diesel engine, the five straw walker 8070 was offered with header widths of 13, 15, 17 and 20ft with a mechanical header reverse and automatic adjustment on uneven ground by means of the hydropneumatic compensator, where the compensating pressure provided by the hydraulic accumulators is matched to the weight of the header to give smooth header suspension and flotation. The grain tank holds 160 bushels, 5640 litres. The 5070 here, belonging to Mr. David Lloyd is cutting wheat on a stock farm at Walton near Presteigne on the Welsh borders, where it also does some contracting in a largely stock rearing area where few farmers grow enough grain to justify having their own combine. The standard transmission was a variable belt system offering four forward speeds, but hydrostatic transmission was an option on this model. The 8070 had the same high performance features as the 8080, but with smaller overall dimensions. The New Holland Rotary Separator feature is standard.

NH 8000

A feature of this series was the all glass cab, three large sheets of tinted glass were stuck together, the cab had no blind spots and the sloping forward angle of the windscreen reduced possible reflections.

THE TF SERIES

Twin Flow technology evolved in 1983, this increased separation capacity. Behind the main drum, the large beater and the Rotary Separator, a 2.37m wide Twin Flow rotor and concave replaced the straw walkers. Together with large concaves with fins it divided the crop into two layers that made 1 and ¼ revolutions before being thrown out on both sides. The grain had plenty of time and space to separate from the straw. Because the crop was separated at a high speed, throughputs and performance were high. The TF 42 and 44 were the first models followed by the TF 46 in the mid 1980's. High capacity headers with optional Auto Float system, which keeps the header parallel to the ground and the header height is automatically set, is retained as on the TX models. They have four speed hydrostatic drive. The Multi Function control lever combines controls for all header functions and hydraulic feed reverser, and engagement of threshing, header and unloading auger is electro hydraulic as on the larger TX models. Other functions such as engine throttle control fan speed, drum speed variator synchronised reel speed and engagement of straw chopper are all electrically controlled in the cab. Powered rear wheels, integrated chopper and chaff spreader were options.

TF 76 ELECTRA

Working at Bowley Farms, Dinmore, Herefordshire, this TF 76 with 7.32m/24ft header is cutting winter barley. These were offered with header widths of 5.18m, 6.10m and 7.32m. The second generation of TF combines were introduced in 1995 with the top of the range TF 78, followed by the TF 76 Electra in 1998. The Electra uses the same high capacity TF separating system as the earlier models, but in addition, differed from the first TF models having increased engine power and more sophisticated electrical systems. Electra was an important step in the application of electrical systems for the transmission of data in a combine. Through fibre optic cables, the operator receives information about the behaviour of components in the combine, instructions to the components can be sent back using the same transmission mode, so that they react better to changing field conditions. Powered by a fuel efficient 6 cylinder turbo charged diesel New Holland 191hp engine, the TF 76 Electra was a high capacity combine with grain tank capacity of 8000 litres which could unload 72 litres a second. The drum and Rotary Separator are the same size, with width of 1.20m. The Discovery cab offers the ultimate in operator comfort and control and low noise levels, including electrically controlled mirrors, pre wired radio and CB with loudspeakers come as standard, the cab is fitted with Info View Monitor.

THE TX SERIES

In 1986, the TX models appeared. They marked the entry of new technology. The self-levelling cleaning shoe was introduced.

Ford had taken over New Holland when the TX range was launched with the TX 34 and 46 in 1986, followed by TX 32 and 36, in the late 1980's and the TX 30 in 1990. The larger TX range consisting of the TX 68 and 66 appeared followed by the 62 and 64 models in the mid 1990's. The last TX model, the 63 was replaced by the CX models in 2005/2006. In 1987, New Holland introduced the Lateral Float system, the first hydraulically operated header control system in the industry.

TX 34

The TX 34 was offered with 15ft or 17ft cutting widths in mechanical or hydrostatic versions, and with either a standard or self levelling cleaning shoe. The self levelling hydro version could have a 17ft or 20ft header. The New Holland Rotary Separator was standard and on this range, the automatic levelling self cleaning shoe on slopes up to 17% was offered as an option, having been introduced on the TX series. The self levelling shoe is suspended on a pivot at the front and supported by rollers on a semi circular rail at the back. The electrical actuator changes the angle of the cleaning shoe to compensate for the tilt of

the combine. On the hydro models, powered rear wheels and rear levelling, an automatic system to raise or lower the rear axle hydraulically to keep the combine level, were options. Controlled electronically, the levelling system maintained a level attitude when climbing slopes up to 22% or when descending hills up to 6%.

— LEFT

TX 34 cutting winter barley near Tenbury Wells Worcestershire.

The model was offered with a choice of a standard cleaning shoe, or with self levelling shoe and as a Hydro model. Powered by a Ford 678HT 6 cylinder 183hp engine, it is a five straw walker combine with grain tank capacity of 6000 litres. The larger grain tank and overall capacity was linked to increased operator comfort and convenience. The cab also became the operational centre from where the driver was in full control of harvesting. This model has a cab with tinted glass, air conditioning and more convenient operator controls, the reel speed was electronically controlled and horizontal reel adjustment hydraulically undertaken from the cab, as well as the drum speed. Features such as a grain loss monitor appeared and automatic header compensation and header reverser were standard. This combine has a straw

chopper in the out of work position as it is swathing the straw. Available as an option on this range, the integrated straw chopper has a straw spreader linked to it. A chaff spreader with contra rotating discs to spread the chaff the full header width was also an option.

The new range of TX combines ranged from 206 to 310hp, and eventually consisted of eight models with some Plus versions. These had more sophisticated technology and more electronic controls, while retaining New Holland proven features such as the Rotary Separator. A new style and updated Discovery cab appeared with large areas of curved glass giving a panoramic view, with InfoView ™ Monitor, Multi control lever and electro hydraulic controls. Auto float appeared which automated the lateral floatation system and the header height control system. All TX models had emissionized engines.

TX 62

The smallest of the next series of TX combines, this TX 62 is cutting spring barley in Herefordshire. A five straw walker combine, it is powered by a Ford 190hp engine, although some did have a New Holland 206hp engine, which was built to comply with emission norms set out by the authorities in 1999. It was offered with cutting widths from 3.65m to 6.10m, and features the main drum with a diameter of 0.606m, and Rotary Separator. Automatic header compensation with auto stubble height control was standard. More electronic controls appeared for easier operation, the reel speed was electrically controlled from the cab and synchronized to forward speed, and fan speed electrically controlled. This model has the Discovery cab with curved glass as standard, which gives an unobstructed 210 degrees view and was said to be the quietest cab on the market at the time. It also had the InfoView ™ Monitor to display information and monitor harvesting operations. The self levelling cleaning shoe became standard on this range. A lever engages the threshing, header, unloading auger and auger swing while on the larger models in the range, this is electro hydraulic. The fuel tank held 450 litres and the grain tank had a capacity of 7200 litres.

TX 66

This combine was available with headers from 5.18 to 7.32m. The combine here has a straw chopper which is in the work position chopping the haulm from beans which it is cutting. The other picture is of it harvesting oats at Wilmaston Farm, in the Golden Valley near Peterchurch Herefordshire. A six walker combine powered by a Ford 260hp engine. Some later models had a New Holland 675/TA/VN 260hp engine. It featured the main drum with a diameter of 0.606m/24in and Rotary Separator the same size. It is fitted with the Discovery cab with a passenger seat, and has Lateral float as standard, and Auto float, a fully automatic header control system which was added to the Lateral float system. This was available on all TX models except the TX 62. Auto float was an option on all TX models except the 62, and standard on the TX 67 and 68. The automatic header compensation system maintains a constant pre-set ground pressure when working with the header in contact with the ground as in laid crops, when the auto height system is overridden and the header height button is selected, the header resumes the pre-set height and an accumulator gives smooth header suspension. Two ultrasonic sensors at the rear of the header constantly measure the distance between their own position and the outer bottom skids. The skids on both sides provide pressure on the ground. The header can be set to a pre selected height which is then maintained automatically. A switch enabled the operator to choose between automatic header compensation and stubble height with or without full auto float system. The grain tank holds 8000 litres, and had a full and 70% grain tank warning device with flashing lights and audible alarm, more warning devices were appearing on combines at this time. This model and the top of the range TX 68 also had electro hydraulic controls for the unloading and auger swing, threshing engagement and header controls. Transmission is hydrostatic with 4 speed gearbox. A standard model of this size with self levelling shoe and without the header weighed 11359kg.

THE TC SERIES

Introduced in 1992 as a model for small farmers, where cost and value for money is a major requirement, it uses one drum and beater and the straw walkers, with the Rotary Separator offered as an option, and were available with Standard headers without all the automatic header controls of the larger models, in cutting widths of 4.6m to 5.2m, using mechanically governed New Holland common rail injection engines with power from 170hp to maximum power of 240hp. There are three five walker models, from TC5060 to 5080, all available as a fixed cleaning shoe or self levelling cleaning shoe version. Two earlier four straw walker models, the TC 5040 and 5050 were discontinued. Offered with choice of mechanical or hydrostatic drive, they have a standard cab with air conditioning as an option rather than standard, and without the electronic technology of the other models. An integrated straw chopper and spreader is an option. Grain tank capacities are from 5200 to 6000 litres. They are used with a choice of High Capacity headers, with options of Control float without lateral flotation, or Autofloat with lateral flotation.

TC 56

The more economic and basic of the New Holland range, the TC is currently available as the TC 56 to TC 58 in fixed cleaning shoe or self levelling version. The TC 54 was the first in the series in 1991, marketed for about ten years until 2002, followed by the TC 56 which was marketed until 2003. The TC 52 was only available for about two years.

It was available with 3.66m to 5.18m headers which had a header reverse system and hydro pneumatic compensation for header flotation over uneven ground. The drum had a 606m diameter and 1.30m long drum. The rotary separator was an option rather than standard as on the TX series. A five straw walker combine, it was offered as a mechanical or hydrostatic combine and it was powered by a New Holland 6 cylinder turbo diesel 15hp engine on the mechanical version or 170hp for the hydrostatic model. The grain tank held 5200 litres. The cab has large areas of glass and the multi function control lever controls forward speed and all header functions, while levers engage the header, threshing system and unloading functions. Performance monitor for grain losses from walkers and sieves was optional, and the self levelling cleaning system and straw choppers were offered as options.

New Holland Rotary models

Ford New Holland as it was known in 1989, with UK headquarters based at Basildon, Essex, were marketing the rotary 205hp TF 42, 44 and 280 hp TF 46 models and the 91hp 8030, 123hp 8055 priced at £51,700 along with the 155hp TX 32, 183hp TX 34 and 240hp TX 36, which was priced at £96,400. The TF 42 rotary had a 208hp turbocharged 6 cylinder intercooled engine.

CX SERIES

The CX Range replaced the TX models in 2001 with a new look. The eight model series was launched by NH in readiness for the 2002 season, these were the CX 720 to 780 with header widths from 3.96m to 7.32m , and CX 820 to CX 880 with header widths from 5.18m to 9.15m. It was combine of the year in 2002.The previous autumn, they were still offering the TC, TX and TF models, but these started to appear out of date when compared to the fancy styling of the new CX series. Machine output was increased without increasing the physical dimensions. It features fully electronic controls with an integrated diagnostic system by this time, the Case Corporation merged with New Holland Belgium NV in 1999, to become CNH Belgium N V in 2002. Engine power ranged from 218hp to 374hp for the top of the range CX 880. A new style header appeared, which retained the Auto float system seen on earlier models, but there were additional improvements, quick couplers enabled hydraulic and electrical connections to be routed though a single socket, making header detachment for transport quicker.

Since their launch, a few engine modifications were made, so they are more efficient and on larger models, a 27hp power boost comes in automatically when the combine is unloading on the move or working at maximum power.

The TX cleaning system and self levelling sieves are retained. In 2001, the CX 720 to 780 and CX 820 were fitted with mechanically governed engines, while the larger CX 840 and CX 860/880 were fitted with full electronic unitised injector engines with a power boost. Later, the smaller models were upgraded to electronically governed engines and by 2005 all mechanically governed power units were phased out, and the following year, the larger 860/880 models had full power at all times instead of a power boost feature.

Sieve settings can now be done from the cab, and there is an integrated yield monitor. The drum and concave has been redesigned, with a drum diameter of 75cm and concave wrap of 111 degrees, with the rear beater and rotary separator also being larger than in previous models.

There was further development in straw chopping systems for residual management. With wider headers and an increase in minimal cultivations or even zero tillage there has been an increasing need for a fine and regular chop and even spreading of straw and chaff to enable a good seed germination and seed growth, which requires maximum contact with the soil. Too much residual straw and chaff left on the ground inhibits contact with the soil and can delay germination of the new seed.

The drum and Rotary Separator seen on the TX models and earlier was still used but repositioned, to ensure a higher capacity throughput.

CS SERIES

The CS was sold alongside the CX range. This was introduced in 2003, and was a smaller capacity combine using three drum technology. The Rotary Separator was optional on the smallest model, the CS 520. It had a wider range of adjustments than the CX, It could be equipped with the Rotary Separator and Multi Thresh systems but in addition to the usual speed and position options, the rear of the Opti Thresh concave of the main drum could be adjusted independently giving more control over straw quality. There was also a hill version, the CL 560, the whole combine kept level on slopes up to 38% on both sides, and 30% when working uphill and 10% downhill. There were four models in all, the CS five walker 540 and six walker 560 were the first followed by the CS520 and six walker CS60. Engines were New Holland 675TA of 204hp to 281hp. And grain tanks had a capacity from 6300 litres to 8800 litres, with unloading speed of 72 litres a second. The drum diameter was 0.607m with 8 rasp bars. These models evolved into the CS 6050, 6060 laterale and CS 6060 hillside and 6080. They were

sold alongside the CSX until discontinued when they were replaced by the CSX.

CSX 7000 SERIES
CSX Range

CSX uses Four Drum Technology. The range was launched around 2006 to replace the previous CS range, the CSX 7080 and 7060 were first two models with 4.57m cut to which the 7040 and 7050 and 7070 added. The new range of CSX models as at 2009 consists of five basic models, three 5 straw walker and two 6 straw walker machines, available with lateral and full Hillside versions with High capacity, and Varifeed ™ headers available.

The CSX range was designed to fill the gap left by the discontinuation of the TX range. Headers are available in widths of 4.0m - 7.32m for the smallest 7040 to 4.57m to 7.32m/24ft for the top of the range CSX 7080.

The Varifeed ™ header new to CSX, has a fore and aft adjustment reach of 500m, made electro hydraulically from the cab. The bottom of the header is closed in all positions without the need for filler plates. Auto Float, and other header features is retained as on CX .

A new generation of engines appeared, CSX are powered by Iveco Cursor 9 engines, built to comply with Tier 111 emissions standards with hp from 242hp for the CSX 7040 to 333hp for CSX7080 (as at 2009). They use Common Rail Technology, which uses a high fuel injection pressure generated in an accumulator-the Rail. The high pressure produces a fine mist of fuel that burns better and cleaner in the combustion chamber, resulting in reduced fuel consumption and lower noise and less exhaust emissions. They comply to Tier 111 standards

CSX models use HarveStar ™ technology, The main 606mm diameter drum has the OptiThresh ™ concave, In addition to drum speed and fine concave adjustment, this new feature first introduced on the CS range, allows the rear part of the concave to be repositioned to adapt threshing to harvest conditions such as grain maturity and yield. The hinged top section can be moved away from the drum to give a softer rubbing action.

Rotary Separator is retained with Multi Thresh ™ System and Straw Flow beater. Harvestar ™ Technology - The new Smart Sieve ™ self levelling system is standard. This off sets the effects of side slopes up to 25% on both sides. Both the pre cleaner and top sieves are controlled by the system moving the slopes laterally, so avoiding grain kernel concentration on the low side.

An electric actuator repositions pivot points on the sieve assemblies depending on the slope, the amplitude of the lateral movement is adjusted.

The Smart Sieve ™ uses the fan speed to recognise grain size Automatic kernel size adaption - it then uses this information via a direct link to the fan speed to adapt the throwing angle for a more precise slope correction. The Discovery Plus Cab is ergonomically designed with air conditioning for more operator comfort and optional air suspended seat, other features include remote controls for all functions and electrically operated mirrors. There are also hillside versions, the CSX75L, 76L and 78L, which have a complete machine side slope levelling system. This is controlled by inclinometers controlling a hydraulic system which lowers and raises the final drives. The Laterale system works on slopes up to 18%, but when used in conjunction with the Smart Sieve ™, the combine can work on slopes up to 30%.

CSX 7060

— CENTRE

This CSX 7060 with 20ft header is cutting oilseed rape at Wilmaston Farm, Peterchurch Herefordshire. Fitted with the Varifeed header, in extended position for harvesting rape, the model is available in cutting widths of 4.57m to 7.32m/24ft.

It has an integrated straw chopper and spreader, which is an option on this model. Powered by a Iveco Cursor 9 maximum 303hp common rail injection engine, it has hydrostatic transmission and uses latest Harvestar technology including the 'Smart Sieve' self levelling cleaning system for efficiency on slopes and Opti Thresh system. Powered rear wheels and a Differential lock were optional. It has the new Intelli View ™ Monitor in colour with more information such as Returns display. The grain tank holds 7500 litres, with an unloading speed of 72 litres a second. The standard Smart Sieve ™ version without header and straw chopper weighs 10,550kg and list price for the 2010 harvest is £186,131, while the Laterale version is £201,731.

CX 8000 SERIES

These 8000 Series models evolved from the CX range launched in 2001, and were sold alongside the TC, CSX and CR ranges and like the predecessors, all built at Zedelgem in Belgium. They were the flagship of the NH conventional combines, available with five walker models the CX 8030 to 8050, and the six walker CX 8060 to 8090. They were an updated version of the CX range, the main change being increased engine power ranging from 272hp to 455hp, and changes in engines to reduce fuel consumption and noise and comply with emission standards to Tier 111. These were powered by Iveco Cursor 9 8.7 Litre 24 valve engines using modern injection technology, the common rail injection system, with engines built to Tier 111 emissions standards. The smallest 8030 was fitted with a new advanced common rail New Holland NEF 6 cylinder common rail engine. The largest 8090 uses a Cursor 10 10.3 litre engine with electronic unitized injectors. This model is reputed to be the largest conventional straw walker combine on the market. The advanced diesel injection system integrates a high pressure pump and nozzle in a single assembly. A new IntelliView ™ 11 Monitor appeared with a colour screen and rotary encoder navigation. There was more emphasis on automatic guidance systems and Precision farm management systems.

New 'SmartSteer' ™ and 'IntelliSteer' ™ automatic guidance systems became available as options, the latter is based on SGPS-Differential Global Positioning System. The series is used with Varifeed ™ headers or High capacity headers. There was also increased grain tank capacity from 7600 litres to 10500 litres. Further operator comforts in the cab appear, climate control is now standard on the larger models with air suspended operators seat optional on the largest. Various Precison Farming packages are offered as options, for yield and or moisture measuring or full package including DGPS Yield mapping and logging, and desktop software. A moisture sensor mounted in the grain elevator can regularly take a sample of grain for measurement of the moisture content. Features such as four drum technology and straw choppers are the same as on previous models. Said to be the largest on the market, the drum is 75cm diameter. Proven New Holland features such as the self levelling system for slopes up to 17%, is retained on this series, where an electrical actuator is commanded by a levelling sensor which keeps the whole cleaning shoe horizontal, including the long grain pan, the pre sieve, top and bottom sieve. Also a feature of the CX range is the cascade cleaning system, where in the pre sieve, the fan gives an additional air blast through the grain as it

falls onto the upper sieve, to aid cleaning.

This range is now marketed as the 8000 series with 14 models from the 8030 to 8090 with options of a fixed cleaning shoe or automatic 17% Self levelling cleaning shoe version for each model.

CX 8040

This CX 8040 is at a farm awaiting delivery to dealers, in exchange for a new model. The CX 8000 series replaced the CX range. The four walker 8040 was offered with headers of 3.96m to 7.32m and had all the automatic reel controls of the earlier CX model.

Powered by an Iveco Cursor 9 common rail injection electrically governed engine

of 326hp, built to meet Tier 111 emission standards, it has a grain tank capacity of 9000 litres with unloading rate of 110 litres a second and the fuel tank holds 750 litres. It uses four drum technology with Multi Thresh ™ system, Intelli Steer ™ now became an option on this range. Transmission is hydrostatic with four speed gearbox. The standard version weighs 12,450kg without the header and chopper and costs new £205,180 with a fixed cleaning shoe.

CX 860

This CX 860 was still waiting to finish some oats near Ludlow in November 2008 after a very difficult and wet harvest. It is has the Varifeed header, and is a six straw walker combine powered by an Iveco F2B 333hp electronically governed engine. Header widths were offered from 5.18m to 9.15m. It features the Discovery cab and has a grain tank of 10,500 litres. The integrated straw chopper can be seen at the rear. This model and the CX 880, uses the four drum technology, with main drum of 0.75m diameter, beater, Rotary Separator and Straw Flow beater with Multi- Thresh ™ concaves. Rotary Separator 0.72m diameter can run at high or low speed. When its extra rubbing capacity is not required, the Multi-Thresh™ system lowers the beater and Rotary Separator concaves. The Straw Flow Beater propels straw onto the first step,

Transmission is hydrostatic with four speed gearbox and electronic gear shifting. The self cleaning shoe was offered as an option, which maintains cleaning capacity on slopes up to 17%.

CX 880

Seen here cutting oilseed rape, this is a six walker combine and was offered with cutting widths of 5.18m to 8.72m. Extra Capacity headers were available as an option from 6.10m to 9.15m. Powered by an Iveco F3A 374hp intercooled engine, the grain tank holds 10,500 litres. It has hydrostatic transmission and Discovery cab. The Straw integrated chopper/ spreader is standard? Two chaff blower units are hydraulically driven, which blow the chaff into the chopper, it is then spread together with the chopped straw. A deflector moved forward allows the straw to be swathed over the integrated chopper. Chaff is blown into the chopper were two hydraulically driven chaff blower units spread the chopped material.

— This Page

M 80 and CX 8060 at Leominster
vintage club working day at Shobdon,
Herefordshire.

CR SERIES

The CR range, a rotary model was developed in 2002 to meet the needs of large scale farmers and contractors who require the highest capacity without compromise in grain quality. They replaced the previous TF rotary combines.

The groundbreaking Twin Rotor ® technology was introduced for the first time by New Holland in 1975 with the TR70 combine model in Grand Island, Nebraska, USA. In 2010 New Holland celebrates 35 years of this technology. Since then over 35,000 combines have been produced with this advanced solution in the threshing and separation process.

The CR Series for the European market have been produced in Zedelgem since 2005, prior to then, they were built in the USA. The CR series is still manufactured in the Grand Island plant and from April 2010 also in the new plant of Sorocaba in Brazil. With more emphasis on fuel efficiency engines were designed with this in mind, and they had a high torque back up of 25%. The load sensing hydraulic pump for the high pressure circuit supplies oil according to demand for threshing, unloading or chopping operations, so reducing power consumption. They were powered by Iveco Cursor engines from 333hp to 428 hp on the CR980, and built to Tier 11 emission levels.

Instead of a drum and beaters, threshing takes place by two longitudinal rotors, 559mm diameter on the CR980, and 2638mm long, the segmented, staggered and spirally mounted rasp bars and separator fins on the rotors repeatedly agitate the crop. The narrower rotors generate a high centrifugal force, the rotor speed and concave clearance are controlled form the cab. Threshing takes place as the crop travels around the rotors which give gentle rubbing action and multi pass threshing, to separate the grains.

The crop is divided into two thin streams. The threshed grains then, move away from the rotors towards the large concaves under the rotors, and then pass through the concave openings, these allow large volumes of grain to be separated from the straw where they pass to the sieves. The CR also has the largest sieve area on the market, 6 and a half square feet. It takes just five seconds for the crop to pass through this combine from entering the feed elevator to discharge at the rear. It is a pure rotary machine, whereas other makes use a conventional rasp bar and concave system. The self levelling cleaning shoe is standard on both CR models. A double roto-thresher, small drums are situated either side of the combine, handles returns, the rethreshed material is returned to the grain pan. A

high capacity double outlet 6 blade fan provides a powerful air blast, the fan speed is electronically controlled from the cab, with the speed displayed in the Infoview ™ Monitor.

The CR uses extensive electronics, the InfoView ™ Monitor informs the operator about all possible harvesting data and settings, factory installed settings for crops can be tailored to suit local conditions, and stored for repeated use. With more emphasis in recent years on fuel consumption, and environmental issues, Precision farming packages are more common on the largest combine models, to reduce seed fertiliser and herbicide costs, and for more accurate spraying rates. The packages offer yield or moisture measuring or both of these plus yield mapping. Data logging is offered and often used on these high capacity models. The fully equipped cab with Info View™ Monitor offers the highest in operator comfort and as on other NH combines is said to be the quietest on the market with noise levels of 76 decibels. Passenger seat, automatic climate control and air suspension seat are standard on the CR. Powered steering wheels are available as an option for use in muddy terrain.

CR 960

This CR960 had the High Capacity 24ft header, and is seen here cutting oilseed rape near Madley Herefordshire. It has a grain tank capacity of 9000 litres, with remote control grain tank covers. A full grain tank of 10,500 litres on the CR980 can be emptied in 100 seconds at 105 litres a second. Powered by an Iveco Cursor electronically governed engine of 333hp, which met Tier 11 emission standards, it had hydrostatic transmission with 4 speed gearbox, and was offered with header widths of 5.18m to 9.15m. Differential lock was standard. The cab was fully equipped with all extras for operator comfort, including air conditioning, automatic climate control, cool box and remote controls for all functions. Powered rear wheels were an optional extra. The fuel tank held 750 litres. An innovative feature was a stone ejection device. A drum at the feeder house entrance regulates the crop flow and ensures that any stones entering the feeder are detected. A deflector plate ejects stones through a pivoting section of the feeder housing bottom, once the stones are detected.

— **ABOVE RIGHT**
CR 9080 and first Claeys combine at Zedelgem.

CR 9080

This CR 9080 is cutting winter barley at Bowley Farms, Dinmore near Hereford. It has a 30ft 10.5m Varifeed header, this model is offered with header widths of 5.18m to 9.15m, in a High Capacity or Varifeed version. The 10.5 35ft header was on trial as a prototype during the 2008 harvest and was available for the first time for the 2009 harvest. It is powered by an Iveco Cursor 13 FPT (Fiat Powertrain technologies) engine with maximum power of 530hp. The grain tank holds 10,500 litres. Threshing is by the Twin Rotors of 559mm diameter and 2638 mm length. The integrated straw chopper and spreader are standard on this model and on the 9090, with 'Opti Spread' for a wider spread of the material. Powered rear wheels and rubber tracks are offered as options. The fuel tank holds 1000 litres.

CR 9000 ELEVATION

The Elevation models, introduced in 2007 for the 2008 harvest, feature a large HP engine, faster rotor speed and different type of straw chopper. They became known as Elevation when CR980 evolved to CR 9000 series, of which the CR9090 is the largest of four models, from 9060, 9070, 9080 and 9090, and currently most powerful combine in the world. These high specification and capacity combines are designed for large scale farmers and contractors who require maximum outputs from their combines, and so can cover larger areas with fewer machines. They are available with header widths of 5.18m to 9.15m with grain tank capacities of 9000 litres to 12500 litres for the flagship model. The CR 9060 is powered by an Iveco Cursor 9 8.7 litre 422hp engine, the CR 9070 Elevation has the Cursor 10 10.3 litre 469hp engine with electronic unitized injectors. The Cursor 13 12.9 litre 530hp engine powers the CR 9080 Elevation while the largest ever engine put on a combine, the 591hp 12.9 TCD engine powers the CR 9090. These engines as on other New Holland combines can now be run on a Biodiesel blend. They are offered with High capacity or Varifeed headers with full automatic header controls, and also feature the Advanced Stone detections system as on the CR 960.

Threshing and separation is the same as on the earlier CR models using twin rotors with a diameter of 432mm on the two smallest models and 559 on the largest two. The Twin Rotor ®system aids separation by creating a large centrifugal force, the rotor speed has been increased on the latest 9000 models. In addition further high cleaning capacity is added with the Opti Clean ™ system, new on the Elevation models. The various parts of the cleaning system, sieves and grain pan give a larger stroke and throwing angle, so that cleaning capacity is higher. The self levelling cleaning shoe is standard on these models rather than an option.

Further developments in straw choppers and spreaders have been made for the CR models, to cater for use with the new 10.7m/ 35ft Varifeed ™ header. The optional Opti Spread ™ straw spreader mounted behind the chopper has two powerful spreading discs to spread over the full width, and can be adjusted from the cab, to allow for side winds and working on sloping ground. There is a choice of four or six rows of knives, those with six rows have knives with impeller characteristics installed at the outer edges of the rotor for high spreading capacity.

Also standard on all CR9000 combines is the IntelliView ™ Soft Key Colour Montior with IntelliView ™ III on the CR 9090. From the 2009 season, all CR combines now have the IntelliView ™ III touch screen Monitor which is DGPS ready.

CR 9090

Currently the most powerful combine with the highest capacity in the world, it is here on the New Holland Stand at Cereals Event, the CR 9090 has a grain tank of 12500 litres. Powered by an Iveco Cursor 13 12.9 litre Turbo Compound diesel engine, of 591 maximum hp, it has the largest engine ever put on a combine. The Turbo Compound engine is a feature of the 9090, this transmits energy left in the exhaust gasses to the engine crankshaft, the Turbo Compound technology consumes less fuel compared to conventional engines, and is able to generate more power. The Twin rotors are 559mm diameter with adjustable cover vanes as standard on this model, to increase crop flow. The updated IntelliView 111 colour Monitor with touch screen is standard. Only available on the CR 9090, the Grain Cam ™ system has a camera which recognises the amount of chaff and broken grain in the sample as it passes through the grain elevator to the grain tank. The information is displayed on the IntelliView monitor in graph form, allowing the operator to fine tune adjustments. The 9090 combine is available with Precision land management systems, SmartSteer automatic guidance, or IntelliSteer used in conjunction with GPS farming packages for yield and moisture recording GPS yield mapping and data logging. IntelliCruise ™ system is an option on all Elevation models, which is an automatic crop feeding system which automatically matches forward speed to the crop load. Sensors on the straw elevator driveline monitor the power demand of the header and feed elevator according to changes in crop flow. This combine has the ultimate in extra equipment, an air compressor for blowing out the radiator and other parts of the combine is also standard. The CR9090 captured the Guinness World Record for harvesting with 551.6 tonnes of wheat harvested in eight hours, in Northumberland in 2008, giving an average rate of 68.95 tonnes an hour in Robigus winter wheat with 17% moisture. List price of the 9090 Elevation with 10.7m header is £371,539, it weighs 16700kg without header and straw chopper. The combine is also available with tracks.

INTERNATIONAL

McCormick had revolutionised agriculture with the invention of the first reaper in 1831. International Harvester was formed at the turn of the century from McCormick Deering and other smaller harvesting companies in the US. IHC in 1968 made combines in Canada, Australia, France, South America and the United States. France made a family of medium to large combines designed for the European market. The International 531 combine was designed and manufactured at Croix France, a suburb of Lille. The covered grain tank, small section bats on the pick-up reel and distinctive platform grain dividers identify it as a European machine.

F8-63

McCormick had made the straight through design B-64 at Doncaster which was similar to the American No 64. An unusual feature of this combine is the 2 in 1 grain tank and begging platform. The F8.63 McCormick International self propelled combine was a tanker /bagger model with a 6½ft header with 7ft gather, with hydraulic control platform. Powered by an International 35hp BD-144A 4 cylinder engine mounted on the top, it had a 6 rasp bar cylinder of just over 18in diameter and three straw walkers. It had a variable speed transmission with three forward and a reverse gearbox, a system of variable speed sheaves and V belts enables the operator to select speed without changing gear. The grain tank capacity was 24 bushels. This combination F8-63 could be switched over from tanking to using the bagging platform in a minute, by unlocking the unloading tube and closing the grain tank outlet. It had a variable speed 6 blade cleaning fan. This machine is in the collection of Mr Ron Knight of Casterton Stamford, where it has been restored to working condition. It was said to have a work capacity of 84 bushels an hour.

INTERNATIONAL 8-51

The 8-51 was the smallest of four models with engine size from 65hp to 105hp, and header sizes from 2.4m/8ft to 4.3m/14ft. Grain tank capacities were from55 bushels to 87 bushels or 3000 litres. They were made from about 1968 to 1972 in France and were superceded by the 31 series. The others in the series were the 8-61 with 75hp engine, 8.71 with 75hp engine and the largest 8-91 which had a 105hp engine.

The four straw walker 8-51 pictured above, dating from with a 8ft header is cutting spring barley near Painscastle on the Welsh borders, where the grain is grown for animal feed on a stock rearing farm. It belongs to International enthusiast Mr Andrew Simmonds. Powered by an International 65 hp direct injection diesel engine, it has a 65 bushel grain tank. The left hand side position of the driver's platform is situated high up on the combine, with the hand controls for engine, hydraulic height adjustment for header and reel, reel fore and aft and speed, and threshing mechanisms situated to the right of the driver. It features the International Triple Returns system, which the manufactures claimed gave a clean grain sample before it entered the tank. In under ripe crops, with little clean grain in the tailings, tailings were returned to the front of the drum for complete re-threshing by using a blocking off plate across the outlet to the grain pan, whereas with a slightly over ripe crop, tailings with mostly threshed crop were returned to the grain pan. Where there was a combination of these two conditions, seen in average crop conditions, a sieve plate was inserted over the outlet of the grain pan, so that the clean grain would fall through to be returned to the grain pan, but the remainder of un-threshed crop was returned to the drum. The grain auger was hinged from transport to working position with the assistance of a spring and locked into position. Hydraulically operated augers were not yet in use on this series.

INTERNATIONAL 3-21

Powered by a sturdy 4 cylinder International IH D-239 engines which were often used in tractors such as the Case 784 and construction equipment machines, the range of combines had a hydraulically controlled ground speed variator with three forward gears. They also had hydrostatic steering. The driver's platform was offset to the left rather than in the centre. It was available in 10ft and 12ft cutting widths.

Made in France, it was sold alongside the 4-31 and 5-31, and was the smallest of the three. A larger 5 straw walker model, the 953 with 6 cylinder turbocharged 140hp engine for higher power and more output, and 4600 litre grain capacity, was later added to the range, this eventually replaced the outgoing 3-21, 4-21 and 4-51 models. Outputs were said to be in the region from 5 to 12 tonnes per hour according to model. The later models were supplied with 825 series headers with wire type dividers with oleopneumatic cutter bar suspension, a tank filled with nitrogen which cushions the hydraulic lift. The 5-51 was available with tracks. Another feature excusive to IH combines at this time was a Triple Returns system for the tailings with a choice of the returns going to the drum, or grain pan, or thirdly to both.

— LEFT

Here Elliot Burman of Madley near Hereford is cutting winter oats with a 10ft 3-21, which is one of the later models manufactured, dating from 1985. This was a simple designed machine making maintenance easy. The 3.9litre engine produces 83hp. The wide threshing cylinder was 41 inches with 18in diameter, and the grain tank held 61 bushels or 2250 litres and the fuel tank 120 litres. Together with an older International 3-21 the combine cuts about 140 acres annually. It had four 'open' type straw walkers. A feature of IH combines were the 'open' straw walkers, which consist of saw tooth blades and removable rods for threshing coarse grains. Steering was hydrostatic.

INTERNATIONAL 4-31

This model was available in cuttings widths of 10ft, 12ft and 14ft, it had a detachable platform with hydraulically controlled header and reel height, and reel speed and horizontal reel movement. This V registered, circa 1980 model has a 10ft header and here Mr Robyn Richards is cutting spring barley near Canon Bridge, Herefordshire. The combine is powered by an International Harvester SAE 92hp 6 cylinder diesel engine, it had four straw walkers and grain tank capacity of 2250 litres. The drum was slightly larger than the 3-21 with diameter of 22 inches. A cab was an option. There were fewer International combines sold in comparison to the MF and Claas models at this time, but it proved a popular combine in this area due to a former local International dealer. The unloading auger was still manually moved into place, but on the two larger models, this was hydraulically operated.

AXIAL FLOW 1460

The Axial Flow 1400 Series. The first generation of Case IH Axial Flows were introduced in America by International Harvester in 1978, using a principle that can be traced back 100 years. Development of the single rotor Axial Flow had been taking place over a period from 1967 to 1977, although the invention of the Axial concept took place during the 1950's up to 1960. During the 1960's, single and double rotor prototypes were compared. The East Moline plant produced the Axial Flow later in 1977, which was made to adapt to many different crops. In 1979, a few were sent to the UK, France and Germany. By 1981 all IH combines were rotary models, with no conventional combines being built. In 1979, the Axial Flow 1400 Series were awarded a gold medal award at SIMA show in Paris. A new factory was built in France where production started in 1983, to meet the demand for Axial Flow combines.

The 1400 series consisted of three models ranging from a 13ft cut 1420 with a 124hp engine to the 210hp 1480 with a 22ft 6in cut. The 1440 and 1460 were introduced in 1977 with an initial run of 300 machines, followed by the larger 1480 in 1978, which had a DT 436 engine, 30ft rotor, 208 bushel grain tank and sieve cleaning area of 4750ft.

The 1440 had a DT 436 IH engine, 24ft rotor, 145 bushel grain tank and 4750sq feet cleaning area. The 1480 had a fuel tank capacity of 123 gal and 1440/1460 had capacity of 92 galls.

A single large rotor spiralled the grain rearward, threshing repeatedly. The speed of the rotor was electrically adjusted on the go. Axial Flow refers to the way in which the crop flows through the threshing mechanism in a direction parallel to the axis of the rotor rather than perpendicular to the cylinder as in a conventional combine. The crop passes between the rotor, concaves and grates several times, instead of once only. An impeller at the front of the rotor starts the crop spiralling rearwards around the rotor, at the same time drawing air and dust in from the front of the feed elevator. As the crop spirals round the rotor, rasp bars thresh the crop. IH thought of this idea on their drawing boards over 15 years before, and prototype testing was undertaken in all crops in North America and Australia for ten years prior to the launch.

All models used three piece concaves of which there were two sizes, the small were for wheat and small grains and the large wire concaves were for corn and other crops grown in the US. In the back half of the rotor cage, there were three separating grates, available in a slotted style for most crops or bar style for conditions requiring more aggressive separation.

— Opposite

AXIAL FLOW 1460

This one was first registered in 1984 and cost new £37,000. The present owner Harvey Beamond bought it for £10,000 in 1994. This 1460 had a 15ft header, and it worked until last harvest and is on a farm at Boraston, near Tenbury Wells, Worcestershire.

Powered by a 170hp DT 436 IH engine, the 1460 had a single 610mm diameter rotor with no drum or concave or straw walkers. The 1460 and 1440 models had three impeller blades and a rotor, while the larger 1480 had four impeller blades. Adjustable vanes on the rotor cage controlled the speed of the crop through the rotor cage area. A four blade discharge beater expelled the crop material coming off the back of the 610mm diameter rotor to a pair of spreaders which spread the material on the ground. The fan was a 6 blade paddle type.

Changes to the Axial Flow models in 1979 included new engine design for the 1440 and 1460 - the turbocharged engines became 'B' series engines. All models are hydrostatic drive only, this ground drive was said to have been pioneered by International Harvester on combines for some years prior to the Axial Flow, which provided infinitely variable ground speed within a three speed transmission and final drive. Axial Flow models were eventually offered with a choice of 9 sizes of header from 10 to 30ft, in the Quick Attach 810 Series.

Cabs were now fitted, and some functions were electro hydraulically controlled with electric instrumentation, a shaft speed monitor was available, the grain unloading auger from the 180 bushel grain tank was hydraulically activated from the cab. It had a twin rotor straw spreader. J I Case Europe then based at Wheatley Road, Doncaster in South Yorkshire had the 1640, 1660 and 1680 available in 1989, for prices ranging from £68,191 for the smallest model to £89,779 for the 1680.

The 1400 Series was succeeded by the second generation of Axial Flow combines, the 1600s in 1986.

The third generation of the US built Axial Flow combines, the 2100 series was launched in 1995, with several new features. In 1985 the merger between Case Corporation and International Harvester agricultural equipment brought IHC Axial Flow combines of recent years under the Case IH banner and models were now known as Case IH.

The new 1030 Series header had the Field Tracker option, which automatically kept the header parallel with the ground, as well as automatic float control and automatic return to cut. Auto reel to ground speed became standard on the 2100 series. 1010 and 1020 headers could also used.

Return to Cut feature appeared- allowing a pre set cutting height to be set, using the AHHC Auto Header Height Control.

Auto Float Control option was available for headers cutting at low heights. The pressure of the hydraulic oil in the lift cylinders was monitored in this mode. When the header started to bulldoze into the ground, the header is lifted up until the cylinder pressure decreases. This was designed for European use and other applications where AHHC was not used.

The single rotor concept with the multiple threshing action with centrifugal separation was the only moving part in the threshing and separating mechanism. The rotor speed was infinitely variable from

the cab. It had a cross flow cleaning fan instead of the paddle type on the earlier 1400 series.

Machine controls and monitors became more sophisticated with more sensors, there were digital read outs for engine RPM, fan RPM and rotor speeds. There were sensors to monitor machine settings, shaft speed - this checked nine drives, rotors, intake elevator, straw chopper and spreaders, fan, shoe, grain and tailings elevators and rotary screen, with alarms to warn of any problems. The 2100 series cab became a command centre for the operator. In the cab, the right hand corner post contained the performance monitor with displays, warning lights and gauges, while other panels had a dual display tachometer and speedometer. Total acres harvested, separator hours and engine hours could be monitored together with other functions such as warnings for low fuel and the unloader auger being left on, battery and coolant etc and shaft speed warnings, grain tank levels, excessive oil temperature hydraulic fluid levels and when the parking brake was on.

Many different problems were encountered in early models of the 2100 series in 1995 and early 1996 and upgrades were made to rectify some of these, including overhauling transmissions and a newer design of feeder lift cylinders. The 2100 Series was replaced in 2002 by the 2300 Series.

— OPPOSITE

AXIAL FLOW 2188

Powered by a 350hp Cummins turbo diesel inter cooled engine, this 2188 with a 20ft 1030 Series header, dates from 1995 and is here cutting winter wheat near Felton Butler Nesscliffe Shrewsbury. It was available with the new 1030 Series headers in widths of 4.3 metres to 6.75 metres, which were designed for the European market, and made by Dronningborg for Axial Flow. Unlike the previous 810 headers which were built in America for the short straw crops there. A new wider cab appeared, with curved glass centred above the feeder house, instead of being mounted off centre with passenger seat with storage under. Heating, ventilation and Air conditioning were redesigned. Temperature is now controlled by an electric sensor located in the HAC coils, with a HVAC Computer and electronic heater valve. The steering wheel could be tilted or pivoted up and down on the pedestal with cab mounts, designed to minimize vibrations and bumps. The control console was no longer mounted on the cab, instead on the operators seat itself where it moves in unison with the seat.

The hydro Multi Function Lever became a mini control centre with header functions, Field Tracker, left/right manual tilt, unloading auger in/out functions and reel functions on it. Other controls were for the parking brake, fan speed rotor

speed two speed hydro and a unique electrical function allowed the unloading mechanism to shut off when it was swung in. This model has a 7400 litre grain tank, with warning lights for when it was nearly full, and flashing beacon alerted the trailer driver, this was common on combines by now.

Axial Flows were fitted with an integrated Straw chopper, which could be changed quickly for swathing, while a chaff spreader was an option.

THE 88 SERIES

The largest of four in the series, consisting of the 5088 to 7088, these new Axial Flow models were launched in 2008 for 2009 harvest, to replace the 2388 X-Clusive models. The latest Case IH combines feature Power Boost technology for top harvesting performance and a range of advanced features and functions. They are available with three header ranges, with automatic header recognition which involves no setting up time when changing headers. The 2000 series grain headers are available in 5.18m 6.1m and 7.32m widths. The 2030 is used for conventional crops while the 2050 has an adjustable knife position which can be moved forward from the cab, for oilseed rape crops.

— THIS PAGE

7088 AXIAL FLOW

Available with optional unloading auger lengths of 5.5m and 6.4m, the 7088 has an unloading rate of 106 litres a second. The 10.570 litre grain tank has electrically controlled folding extensions. The Cross Flow cleaning fan is retained from the 2188 series. In the cab, post instruments give information on everything from engine power, header tilt, residue direction electrical sieve settings to service reminders and diagnostics. The multi function lever controls all the header functions, unloader swing and engage and

emergency feeder and header shut-off. Threshing with the single rotor of 762mm diameter is the same concept as the previous models, only the rotor is larger.

Powered by a Case IH 9 litre 366 maximum hp engine, with electronic fuel injection, the 7088 engine has been designed to meet recent environmental standards, the turbocharger is built into the engine design, with inlet and outlet

manifolds on opposite sides creating a cross-flow of gases for optimum efficiency and low emissions, so they are Tier 111 compliant, it is quiet and can deliver extra power when needed for chopping, and unloading. Transmission is hydrostatic with three variable speed ranges.

Case Advanced Farming Systems is an option on this model with features such as automatic crop settings, rotor and

fan speed, sieves and concave clearance for individual crops, together with Accu Guide automatic steering system. Powered rear axle is an option, but the 7088 has a heavy duty adjustable steering axle as standard. An integrated chopper with 76 fine cut knives and spreader are standard equipment.

AXIAL FLOW 9120

The latest American built 20 series range with the flagship 9120 model claims to be the biggest combine in North America, having the highest hp, a 523hp engine, and 350 bushel grain tank. This model has now made its debut in Britain. It is the largest of three in the series, the others being the 7120 and 8120. The series was launched in 2007 with the 9010 was then the largest, with 13 litre 530hp engine and grain tank of 10500 litres. In 2009, the 9020 was introduced in the UK. There are two header ranges, the 2030, and 2040 with an additional clearance between the knife and the auger. A feature now common on larger combines is a self cleaning engine air screen. The flat stationary engine air screen features a hydraulic driven rotating wand evacuation fan which pulls material off the surface of the screen to keep a direct airflow to the engine and cooling systems.

On demonstration from West Midland Tractors, agents for Case IH, this 9020 is put through it spaces at Bayston Hill, Shrewsbury, Shropshire in winter wheat. The threshing concept is the same as on previous Axial Flow models except that a new designed ST -Small Tube rotor of 762mm diameter is standard on the 9020, with a 'hard thresh' feature - twice the number of raps bars to thresh out unwanted caps in small grains. In addition to the Cross Flow fan, a standard feature on the 9020 is the X-tra force cleaning system, this features a self levelling system which includes the grain pan and cross flow fan to cope with side slopes of up to 15%, so giving a higher capacity. It has a 10,580 litre grain tank which unloads 113 litres per second. The machine is fitted with a 126 blade chopper for precision cutting. Powered by a Case IH 13 litre turbocharged and intercooled engine, the 9020 uses Power Plus CVT drive technology to power the rotor, feeder and header, using a belt free driveline. A feature of this combine is that all the principal power transmission is achieved without use of belts, avoiding problems of wear, slip and replacement. The rotor also has a CVT gearbox, giving a smooth build up of speed. It is seen here with the new 3050 size header, 35ft width, with an increased adjustable knife position up to 57cm. The model could be used with the 2000 series headers from 6.1 up to 9.15m.

Full Advanced Farming systems are available, and Cruise Cut is installed on this 9020, a laser controlled auto guidance system. It has a fully equipped luxury cab. It weighs 16624kg without header. List price for 2010 is £283,042 with 10.7m header.

DEUTZ FAHR

Fahr combines were imported into the UK by Watveare Overseas Ltd from Ivybridge Devon.

The M66 and M66S, M88 and M88S were earlier models, followed by the M600, M900, M1000, M 1100, M1200, M1300, and M1600. Livery was orange red with Fahr logo.

The M900 replaced the M885 in 1973. This had a 9ft 6in cutting table, 40in wide drum with 22in diameter and 4 straw walkers, using a Deutz 4 cylinder 71 hp engine. The first Fahr combine had been produced at Lauingen in 1971, the second factory taken over by Fahr for combine production.

The next series, the M922, M1002, M1102, M1202, and M2480 became known as Deutz-Fahr, but were still the orange red colour. The M1300-1302, M1302H, M1600H followed from these - the 1300 and 1600 were available as Hydrostatic H versions. Development started on a combine with hydrostatic drive in 1962 at the Fahr Lauingen plant, by 1965, they were successful in tests, and the Hydromat, the first combine with hydrostatic drive appeared in 1966.

The M2580 and M2680 also appeared, from circa early 1980's.

Other models sold at this time under Deutz Fahr were the M66TS, M660, M770.

— ABOVE
DEUTZ FAHR 1610H

Cutting oilseed rape on the farm of Paul and Gary Jones, Tredomen near Brecon, Wales, this six straw walker Hydromat - hydrostatic transmission combine with 18 ft header dates from 1985 and was powered by a Deutz 8 cylinder F 8L413 V type 203hp air cooled engine, it had a grain tank capacity of 5000 litres. It was available in cutting widths of 3.60m, 4.20m, 4.80m and 5.60m headers had an electro hydraulic cutter guide system, to enable the header to follow the ground contours. Threshing was by a 600mm diameter drum, with a straw stripper drum roller behind it, and 2 axial flow fans for air draught. It had a deluxe cab with electronic function monitoring of machine functions, Steering was hydrostatic. The drum diameter was 600mm with variable speed drive controlled form the driver's seat. A straw chopper was an option. The grain tank held 5000 litres.

DEUTZ FAHR 2780

This 2780 with 14ft header once cut several hundred acres a year together with an identical machine, before bought by John Morgan of Bage Court Farm, Dorstone, where it is seen here cutting winter barley. It dates from 1985, but was a new model offered at the same time as the 1610, with a few modifications and new style cab. A five straw walker combine, it is powered by a 6 cylinder Deutz air cooled engine of approx 150hp, and was available in cutting widths of 3.0m, 3.60m and 4.80m, with header compensation through a pressure accumulator. Transmission was hydrostatic and it features the Deutz Commandor cab with tinted glass, which was sold as an option. There were some electronic functions, for grain levels in the tank, speed control for the straw walkers and returns elevator.

The 35/36 series was introduced in 1981, with additions later, five new models announced in 1985 for the following season were the M35.80M and H, M36.10H, M36.30H and the 225hp M36.30HS were an amalgamation of new features and the proven technology in the established 80 and 1600 series machines and eventually replaced the M2780, M1610 and M1630 which were to be phased out. These new models had the 21 function performance monitor, electrical ground pressure sensor and Deutz Fahr Commander cab, and tandem cutting system, where the

knife sections were positioned bevel-up, bevel-down alternatively along the blade, together with the design of the fingers which had no ledger plate, was said to increase cutter bar life. Biso straw choppers were a factory fitted option.

In 1989, the Fahr importers, Watveare Ltd of Westbury, Wiltshire had the mechanical M34.80, M35.40, M35.75 to M 35.80M on offer, to the hydrostatic models, M35.80 HTS, M36-10H to M 36-40HTS with some available as HTS versions. These were now in Deutz green livery.

DEUTZ FAHR 36-40

A Hydromat model dating from the 1980's one of the M series, this one is waiting in J M T Engineering Warwickshire, for resale or breaking for spares.

The Starliner and Topliner models appeared in the 1990's.

4040 STARLINER

Starliner was introduced in 1992 it was a more basic model than the Topliner, a MD series with a medium power range.

This five straw walker 4040 with mechanical transmission is working in the Kinlet district near Cleobury Mortimer area in Shropshire, and was developed at the Deutz Fahr works at Lauingen Germany. The '5' version had hydrostatic drive. It was offered with header widths of 3.00m to 5.40m with Poly Tine reel with flexible tines, and the standard header adjustments and electric reel speed control, and was powered by an Air cooled Deutz 6 cylinder 140hp engine. The grain tank held 5700 litres. The Master-Vision' cab had air conditioning, and standard fittings, with no passenger seat, Agrotronic C Deutz Fahr electronic monitoring system monitored machine functions from the engine temperature to the threshing speed. A Master shift joystick integrated into the armrest operated the main machine functions. An integrated straw chopper and automated slope compensation were optional. This model was later replaced by the Ectron

The following year the Powerliner series was launched.

4075 HTS TOPLINER

Introduced in 1991, it was offered in cutting widths of 3.60m to 7.20m this Topliner is in a Same Deutz dealer's yard at Mr Jim Price of Newington, Craven Arms, Shropshire. It is a 6 straw walker machine powered by a Air cooled 6 cylinder 240hp Deutz engine. A feature of this combine was the TS Turbo Separator technology, introduced in 1989, a drum with diameter of 590mm, which enabled constant threshing speeds in green or damp straw, which followed the main drum of 600mm. It has the Commandor 11 cab, with air conditioning, refrigerator compartment, 3 stage fresh air blower, ergonomic driver's seat and co driver's seat, electronic setting for table, threshing unit, grain tank emptying, and straw chopper. There were some electronic monitoring systems, such as electronic speed monitoring of straw walkers, grain and overshot elevator. The grain tank held 6500 litres. The Deutz Fahr Agrotronic information device gave optical and acoustic monitoring and warnings for 23 functions. The Topliner 'Balance' system introduced in 1995, gave fully automated slope compensation up to 20% on lateral inclinations, due to automatically compensating final drives, and uphill and downhill gradients up to 6%. A cutter bar trolley was an option as well as rape side knives and integrated straw chopper.

5660 HTS

This is one of four straw walker models in the 50 Series, the 5650H, 5660HTS, 5680H and 5690HTS TS denoting Turbo Separator. It is seen here cutting oilseed rape at Brobury near Bredwardine, Herefordshire. It was available in cutting widths of 4.20m to 6.30m, with header Autocontrol as standard, which adjusted lateral positioning and height of cutter bar. Threshing is with a 600mm diameter main drum, and the third Turbo Separator drum with diameter of 590mm, which is standard on this HTS model. Powered by a liquid cooled Deutz 6 cylinder 260hp engine, this five walker combine is a hydrostatic model with variable speed control with 4 speed transmission. It features a new Commandor 111 Cab, complete with full aid conditioning, Commandor control for electrical operation of header, thresher, concave and grain tank discharge, and a standard throughput monitor. The on board computer is standard on HTS models. The grain tank holds 7500 litres. This series has now been replaced by the 60 Series for 2010.

The 60 Series was launched in 2009, with new styling, load sensing hydraulics and revamped shaker shoe. This Series is available as the 6060H and 6060HTS to 6095HTS versions, with three models with the 'Balance' slope compensation system.

The range starts with the 6060H with 250 hp Deutz engine and grain tank capacity of 7500 litres to the top of the range 6095HTS with 366hp engine and 8500 litre grain tank with headers widths from 5.4m to 6.3m.

— RIGHT

This six walker combine is on display at Agritechnica launched 2009 for 2010 harvest, the 6090HTS is available in cutting widths from 5.4m to 7.2m and is powered by a Deutz 310hp engine and has a grain tank capacity of 8500 litres. List price is £178,800. Threshing is with a main 60cm diameter cylinder, and beater and a third peg drum of 59cm, the Turbo Separator. The fan is an adjustable Cross Flow type.

LAVERDA

M112

The M112 was sold alongside the M92, M132 and M152 during the later 1970's this range followed the M84, M 110, M120, M 150 range which was available in the 1976 season. They were marketed by Bamfords of Uttoxeter, Stafford. Laverda had replaced the Allis-Chalmers combines under the Bamford name in the early 1970's.

The M112 was the third model introduced in a new line of Laverda combines, following the M132 and M152. Although never the most appealing to look at, Laverda combines were known for their rugged reliability, high output and clean grain quality in the larger combines. A feature in common with the first two models is the provision of safety guards for external mechanisms, which comply with international safety regulations.

Many combines still lacked adequate safety guards at this time. The M112 was also available as an AL version.

The driver's platform was in a central position, and a feature of this range is the centrifugal blower which acts over the upper part of the header and blows dust away from the operator. Powered by a six cylinder engine with a power output of 95hp -70kw, it had a large 600mm diameter drum. It was offered with header

widths of 10ft, 12ft and 14ft and had a rain tank capacity of 2650 litres or 75 bushels which could be increased with grain tank extensions. Power was transferred to the threshing mechanism by a Pow4erband belt and to the traction mechanism by means of V belts with hydraulically controlled variator.

LAVERDA 152

Introduced with the M132 in the mid 1970's, it was available with 12ft, 14ft and 16ft cutting widths.

Seen here at Broadfield Court, Bodenham near Hereford, this Laverda 152 still cuts three hundred acres on this arable dairy farm. Mr Mark James bought it eight years ago to replace a M150 which he had new from local dealers Burgess, who were agents for Laverda. The M150 was kept for spares, being almost identical to the M152. It is harvesting wheat here. It was the first model in a new range in the mid 1970's and came with choice of header widths from 12ft, 14ft and 16ft, with the same header functions as on the smaller M112. It has a 14ft header. A Fiat 6 cylinder diesel 130hp-96kW engine provided the power for this five straw walker combine. The grain tank held 94 bushels, this combine was capable of quite a high output at this time, threshing was with a 600 mm diameter drum. There were a few electric warning systems on this model, an electro acoustic signal warned the driver when clutches became engaged for returns auger or when the clutch pedal was actuated while the parking brake was on. However, they did not have the complicated electro hydraulics of later combines, so were simple to maintain, and the body work-sheet metal being galvanised has meant that many have survived and are still working.

The unloading auger was swung back hydraulically whereas on the smaller M112 was mechanical. A cutter bar trolley was an option, which could be towed behind the combine. Weight of the combine with 14ft header was 7385kg. Parts are still made for the older Laverda combines, at San Mateo in Italy.

3850

This was the second largest of the 3000 series combines. It is working near Burley Gate Allenswick, Herefordshire, this six walker combine dating from the 1990's it was bought second hand in 1992 by the present owner. It has a 16ft header. A straw chopper was added to it at a later date. A larger capacity combine, it was offered in cutting widths of 4.20m, 5.40m and 6.00m with a 'C' type header and feeder reverser and hydro pneumatic table suspension. Threshing was with a large heavy 8 bar 600mm Diameter drum. Power came from a Fiat 8361 SI 10 Turbo diesel 6 cylinder engine of 175hp, and transmission was mechanical with hydrostatic steering. One feature of the larger Laverda combine was an automatic stone trap which rejected material that may damage the straw elevator or threshing mechanism an alarm system

alerted the driver in the cab. This was not so common on combines at this time. The rear straw walker shaft could also be set in two positions giving different inclinations to the straw walker surface. The 3850 was regarded as a high output combine that had a 6500 litre grain tank situated between cab and engine. Laverda combines were known by users to be easy to maintain, with maintenance points easy to access, and had a simple design. The air conditioned cab with monitoring instruments for engine and combine performance was now standard in this model. Laverda had introduced combines with electronically controlled functions from the early 1080s, this model had monitors for grain losses from the walkers and sieves and machine function warning lights and indicators on the control panel.

3790

Laverda built a new plant in Breganze and began a partnership with Fiat, which unfortunately was doomed in the last 20 years. This plant produced the M182, the first model equipped with electronically controlled functions. The Fiat Agri group was the result of an amalgamation of Fiat Trattori, Laverda, Hesston and Braud. They brought out new models the 3000 series in 1983, with the 3850 being unveiled in 1984. Based at Bury St Edmunds, Fiatagri UK Ltd marketed the 3400, 3750, 3790, 3850 and 3890 straw walkers models in 1989, and MX240 and MX300 rotary models. Prices in 1989 ranged from £41,820 for the 75hp 3400 model to £82,065 for the largest 148hp 3890 walker model. The driver's seat is off set to the left on this model, instead of being central as on the M112, and these models were still sold without cabs.

In 1984, Fiatagri launched the 3550, a four walker combine with a new 6 cylinder 130hp Fiat engine, for the following harvest. With header width choices of 3.1m, 3.6m and 4.2m, this superseded the 3450 model, and a higher output 3890 based on the 3850, replaced the 3900 model at the top of the range. This had a 200hp Fiat engine and new hydrostatic transmission and header widths of 4.8m, 5.4m and 6m.

This machine is still working in the Ludlow area, it has just finished a field of

wheat at Henley near Ludlow, Shropshire.

Laverdas design philosophy resulted in reliability, easy maintenance and low running costs. Now under the FiatAgri ownership, whose marketing headquarters was at Bury St Edmunds. Laverda were still popular combines in this area having a high capacity combined with simplicity and rugged reliability. They were available in the late 1980's and early 1990's. Drum size was 600mm with width of 1346 mm. Many new ones at the time were sold by local dealers Burgess in this locality, who were agents for FiatAgri Laverda combines. This was offered with cutting widths of 3.60m, 4.20m 5.80m to 6.60m and a Fiat 175hp turbo charged diesel engine provided the power for this five straw walker combine. This model had hydrostatic transmission with four speeds.

LAVERDA M304LS

Manufactured at Breganze in Italy, this is one of the recent models, comprising the 304, 305 and 306 with 304 and 306LS with 4 wheel drive versions. There are also the smaller 225REV models and 255ls and LCS models powered by Iveco engines, and 296 LCS and LS models.

Laverda had first developed the system for working on sloping ground in the early 1990's. The M304LS is the latest version with their self levelling system, which enables automatic levelling up to 20% laterally and 8% fore and aft.

— ABOVE RIGHT

This M304LS is cutting winter wheat in the Middleton Scriven area Bridgnorth Shropshire, and is a self levelling model. It is offered with header widths of 4.80m to 7.60m. Grain tank holds 9000 litres, which can be emptied at a rate of 105 litres a second. It is powered by a Sisu diesel 275hp engine using common rail technology, transmission is hydrostatic with 4 wheel drive.

This M Series model also has a Special Power version which has a new Free Flow header with large intake auger, newly designed pick up reel and integrated with the GSAX electronic system, ground self alignment extra, and MCS Multi Crop Separator. The Commodore cab has air conditioning, and on board Agritronic plus computer. The Ceres 8000i using DGPS

technology for humidity, weight and crop yields is an option. Threshing is with a 600mm diameter drum, followed by a beater and MSC Multi Crop Separator, a 600mm peg drum with retractable tines. The grain tank holds 8200 litres.

— BELOW RIGHT
255LCS

This LCS version is on display at Agritechnica, Hannover Germany. A five straw walker combine, it is powered by an Iveco 245 gross hp engine, it is available in cutting widths of 4.8m to 7.6m and the grain tank holds 7000 litres. The LCS version has the Option Four feature, a device where the levelling function can be used in the crosswise direction only, without moving the body of the combine longitudinally. Features are similar but without the higher specification of the M Series. Threshing is with main 600mm drum, beater and second peg drum of the same diameter.

RANSOMES

This MST 42 is in the collection of Ron Knight from Casterton, Stamford Lincolnshire where it has been completely restored. Ransomes imported the Bolinder-Munktell trailed combine in order to meet the demands of their customers, which they sold as the Ransomes MST 42, for use with a 25hp tractor. These were then made under licence at Ipswich by Ransomes for the 1954 harvest. It was an economical harvester with low operating and maintenance costs, and cost new with standard fittings £577 in 1955. It was a trailed model with 4ft cutter bar and 42in wide threshing cylinders, with bagging platform under a two spout grain hopper. The drum size was 17½in diameter and according to trials carried out by the State Agricultural Machinery Testing Institute, it averaged 60 bushels an hour in wheat and 80 bushels in oats. It weighed 1 ton, 6cwt and 14lb.

In 1959, the MST56 replaced the MST 42, which was available as a tanker or bagger model with a wider 5ft cut but the same drum appeared.

RANSOMES 801

The 801 launched in 1963, followed on from the previous 901, it was similar in appearance, but was a new machine, the engine was on top of the combine rather than underneath as on the 901. By the early 1960's, demand for the trailed MST was falling, the 801 was the follow model.

This combine belongs to a collector near Bridgnorth, Shropshire and has been restored to working condition for vintage harvest events. The 801 was sold alongside the larger capacity 1001 model with 10ft and 12ft cut, which eventually replaced it. It was available as a bagger or tanker model with an 8ft cutting width and a Reynolds 6 bat pick up reel which had an infinitely variable speed range and adjustable tines. Grain tank capacity was 40 bushels, and the output was said to be up to 3 tonnes an hour. Powered by a Perkins 4 cylinder diesel 42.5hp engine, it had a two speed gear box and reverse gear and threshing took place by an 8 inch diameter and 36in wide threshing drum with straw walkers. The new 801's Handi-Matic control system enabled the driver to select drum speed, reel and ground speeds from the drivers' seat. An automatic floating table with twin hydraulic rams was a feature of this model.

RANSOMES CRUSADER

The Crusader was launched at the Smithfield Show in 1967. A feature of this combine is that it had a twin drum threshing system, the front drum having a width of 45in with diameter of 8¾in, followed by the main drum of the same width but larger diameter of 18in. The twin drum idea was said to have been first developed by Ransomes in the 1960's, but later disappeared from the market in Britain with the last of the Ransomes Super Cavalier combines built at Ipswich in 1976, only to be reinvented by other manufacturers in the next decade.

Offered with header widths of 10ft and 12ft, this was a four straw walker combine powered by a Perkins diesel 4 cylinder 74hp engine with a three speed gearbox and reverse gear, hydraulically operated by variable speed pulleys. This Crusader is still working at Caeronen Farm Three Cocks in Powys where Mr Gwyn Jones cuts about 40 acres annually on his stock rearing farm. It is cutting oats here. Dating from 1974, this is a 10ft model. It has a grain tank capacity of 65 bushels and was said to be capable of harvesting 7½ tons and hour. Price new with a 10ft cut when it was launched was £2,995 but the cost increased to nearly double within five years.

B M VOLVO

Volvo B M emerged from several complicated mergers and takeovers by companies known as Munktell, Thermaenius, Bolinder Munktell, Aktiv, and B M Volvo. And at one time they were also known as Volvo B M.

Volvo BM bought the Ava-Thermaenius company in 1960 as a result of Bolinder-Munktell Eskilstuna in Sweden, which was a part of Volvo, deciding to become a farm machinery manufacturer, offering a full range of farm equipment. At this time, the three straw walker Ava ST257 was still produced and imported to the UK, with many being sold from the Kings Lynn branch.

AVA SP 257

This three straw walker SP 257 belongs to collector Mr Keith Williams from near Llandrindod Wells Wales. It was available as a tanker or bagger combine, the reel and 7ft or 8ft cut table were hydraulically controlled, and had a 22in diameter drum and Perkins C4/99 4 cylinder 35hp diesel engine and 39 bushel grain tank. It was an easy to operate small combine for use in

both small and large fields. The larger straight through S 1000 A had a 6 cylinder 80hp Volvo-Penta diesel engine, four straw walkers, and was available with 10ft or 12 ft cutting widths, and grain tank capacity of 55 bushels with optional bagging off equipment.

Under Bamfords, sales of the Volvo BM combines increased, especially for the smaller ST 257 , as well as harvesters originally made by BM, the S1000 and S1000 A models

B M VOLVO S 950

Viking Farm Machinery also became importers of the Volvo BM combines. After a deal was made with Viking, including the S950 were marketed by Bamfords of Uttoxeter until the 1970s. This S950 combine made its debut in the 1960s, and belongs to Alan Johnson, from Tarleton Southport Lancashire where it still used annually. Here it is cutting winter wheat.

It was sold alongside the three straw walker S830 from Bolinder-Munktell and was described as a light weight machine with a high capacity, it had a 44 bushel grain tank, 9ft cutting width, Perkins 4.154 56hp engine and an optional bagging off

attachment. This larger four straw walker S950 with 66 Imp bushel grain tank came in 10, 12 and 14 ft cutting widths, and had a powerful Volvo D50 6 cylinder 117hp engine and large 2ft diameter drum providing a fly wheel effect with high inertia giving a high output. By 1971 Volvo imports ended when Bamfords entered into Allis Chalmers machinery. Production continued until the early 1970's. Volvo BM combines ceased production in the 1980's.

MODEL M

The Avtiv Model M was imported from Sweden by Western Machinery of Ivybridge, Devon and was capable of a very high output. This was one of the last trailed combines on the British market.

Manufactured by A B Westasmasker Morgongava Sweden, it has a 5½ft cutter bar and it is a straight through design which could be pto driven by any medium size tractor. It was available as a bagger or tanker version, the tanker version could hold 33 bushels and the bagging platform could carry 10 cwt of grain on the sacking platform. The machine weighs only 24 cwts. The Activ combine was belt driven throughout with four safety clutches. Threshing was with a 4ft wide 1ft 5in diameter drum, and separating with two adjustable riddles, and cleaning was provided by a four blade fan. Adjustment of the riddles was carried out independently by a lever which alters the position of the tongues. So increasing or decreasing the openings.

— Left

Activ Model M Bagger Model.

Avtiv trailed Andrew Rogers, from Sollars Hope, Ross-on-wye came from Knighton on the Welsh borders, where it was still in use for cutting barley two years prior to Andrew purchasing it about five years ago from a farm sale at Walton near Kington. This model is a bagger version.

— Bottom Left

Active Model M with bagging off platform cutting wheat at Leominster Vintage Club's Annual Working day held at Shobdon, Leominster, Herefordshire. It belongs to Kevin Norris of Alveley, Bridgnorth, Shropshire who has restored it to working order. It originally worked at a farm on the Welsh borders.

— Below

Active Model M Tanker version.

This came from the Bewdley area and dates from 1959. It last worked in 1992 where it had been on the same farm since new. It was bought for restoration by a collector from the Bridgnorth area in 2009.

ACTIV 800

Made by AB Westerasmaskiner of Sweden, this Activ 800 had been tested in the difficult harvest of 1965. It is a self propelled combine and was seen on a farm near Skenfrith Monmouthshire and changed hands when it was sold for restoration to Carmarthen district in Wales. It was sold new by L P Morris of Craven Arms, Shropshire, it is thought that it was sold to a farmer called Reynolds in South Shropshire. The companies name is clearly visible on the combine. A three straw walker tanker combine, a bagging off platform was available. It had an 8ft fully floating header balanced by two helper springs with hydraulic lift for table and reel and also had an emergency header brake. Threshing was by a 19 ½ diameter drum, and a Perkins Diesel 4 107 40hp engine provided the power. The grain tank held 40 bushels and the fuel tank 17 gallons. The straw walkers in three parts were open underneath. It was said to be able to harvest up to 4 tons an hour depending on conditions. The drivers's platform was off set to the left. One feature is that grain lifters were an option, these became standard with headers on most later combines. A straw chopper made by Reckford and Sparman was optional. There were no electronic functions, the fan speed was altered by an external variator handle on the side of the combine.

ALLIS CHALMERS

— ABOVE

By appointment to Her Majesty the Queen: Bamfords the marketing company for Allis.

Super C Gleaner

This was sold alongside the Super A Gleaner, launched also in 1964, it had a larger grain tank, with larger elevators and unloading auger, but other features and improvements were the same. The control panel was also redesigned. A feature of the Allis Super A and C combines was the 'down front' cylinder placed further forward than on most combines, and also the retractable finger beater between the intake auger and the main drum. The finger beater combed and fed the crop directly from the main auger to the sown front drum. There were no long chain raddles or conveyor between the header auger and the cylinder. The threshing cylinder was raised and lowered hydraulically with the table. The sales brochure of the time states that safety guards cover all external working parts, many combines in the 1950's and early 1960's lacked guards over moving belts and pulleys.

SUPER C

This Super C with 10ft cut is cutting barley near Llandrindod Wells, Wales, It belongs to Keith Williams, who still uses it every year to cut a small acreage of barley for a neighbour on a stock rearing farm. It is a 1968 model and came originally from Ditton Priors Shropshire, costing in the region of £2,500 new.

It had a Perkins 6 cylinder 305 84hp engine and three speed gear box with power assisted steering. Threshing was by a 19½ diameter drum with eight rasp bars. It was available in 10ft, 12ft and 14ft header widths. The header body was galvanised before being painted which is one reason why the combine is still in use with very little rust on it. The grain tank held 82 imperial bushels. The Allis Super C combines were popular in the region during the late 1960s many were sold by past dealers T K Philips of Castle Works Wigmore.

ALLIS SUPER C

An unusual feature was the auger being positioned further forward behind the knife, where the retractable auger fingers feed the crop into a feeder beater, behind the auger. This feeds the grain and straw directly and evenly into the cylinder.

ALLIS GLEANER SUPER A

Made from 1964-1971, it followed on from the Model A Super Gleaner, and was launched at the 1964 Smithfield show. It had a new appearance, with new sheet metal work giving it a longer and lower profile. Improvements were made to the grain tank unloading auger in later models and in 1968 it had a four cylinder Perkins engine. It was available as a bagger or tanker combine which held 50 Imperial bushels in the grain tank.

This was manufactured at Essendine Stamford, and is a smaller combine than the Super C. This combine was the first tanker combine in Pembrokeshire and had spent all its working life on the same farm at Pontfaen near Fishguard, since it was new in 1965. It had been parked up since 1980, until bought for restoration in 2009, by collector Kevin Norris from Bridgnorth, Shropshire. These combines were built on a steel chassis, with galvanised and Zintec treated steel sheets, so these combines have not suffered with rust deterioration as many other machines have. It has a Perkins 6 cylinder P6 64203 engine (70hp 305 according to sales brochure) and 8ft 6in header. The fuel tank was repositioned, earlier versions of the Super A, the Model A version had the fuel tank on the left side rather than on the right as on this combine. A feature of the combine is the grain returns elevator which returned the grain directly to the header intake auger. The combine had three straw walkers, a drum width of 30in and diameter 19¼ inches and was offered with alternative header widths of 10ft and 14ft and a bagger model was still an option. The quick detachable header had hydraulically controlled cutting height and the reel was also hydraulically controlled. A floating header with new pressurised compensator to protect the cutter bar from damage on rough ground was now an option.

As with other Gleaner models, it featured a 'down front' threshing cylinder. Space used for feeding on other combines is used for separating in the Gleaner.

ALLIS CHALMERS 5000

This was the last Allis-Chalmers British combine built and sales did not take off. Production ceased after the Bamford takeover of Allis in 1971. With a new appearance, it was made from 1968-1971, following tests during the 1967 and 1968 harvests but remained on the market for the 1972 harvest. Its first season was the 1969 harvest, using many features from the former models such as two fan cleaning system, three speed gear box and drum position.

— Right

Alan Yarnold is cutting winter barley here with an Allis 5000 at Upper Sapey Worcestershire. First registered in 1972, it was bought fifteen years ago for £500 and now cuts between 60 and 100 acres a year. It came from Abbots Bromley district in Staffordshire originally. This one dates from around 1970. Production of Allis Chalmers combines ceased soon after. It was fitted with a Cab Craft cab at a later date.

This was a large combine, having four longer straw walkers, heavy duty open-grate concaves, and powered by a larger 103hp Perkins 6 cylinder 354 diesel engine. Steering was hydrostatic. The 5000 was replaced by the Italian Laverda combines sold under Bamfords name. An unusual feature of the 5000 was in addition to the 'Down Front' position of the main drum, there was an exclusive wide grain conveyor, which featured 'cell' formation for the movement of grain from the threshing drum to the sieve shoe, this new Allis Chalmers feature was said to be an advantage on sloping fields. There was a rubber belt added to take the crop up to the riddles. This was not on the Super A and C models. It was available with 10, 12 and 14ft headers, which were Quick Attach as a standard feature since 1966. Flotation was by means of a nitrogen pressure accumulator fitted to the hydraulic circuit, this was first fitted to Allis combines in 1962. Other header features included a throw out clutch for stopping the header in emergency and hydraulic header and reel height control, although fore and aft reel movement was undertaken with a spring loaded belt tensioner. Threshing was with a 40in wide drum and the combine had an 82 bushel grain tank.

— Below Left

Two Allis 5000's at end of life in derelict shed near Henley, Ludlow, Shrosphire. One worked near Euden George in the Bridgnorth area originally before being sold on to the farmer here.

LELY VICTORY

Lely purchased Fisher Humphries in the mid 1960's and production then moved to Wootton Bassett, when they launched the MK II design. The folding header was retained, in 14ft or 18ft cut, and there were improvements to machine design. The combine had an output of 17 tonnes an hour, and the Victory was claimed to be the world's largest combine. Lely was a pioneer of hydrostatic transmission.

The British built Lely Victory Mark II and Mark III, which were later models, were the only models in the world at one time in the 1960's with folding headers, where two hydraulic rams were used to fold the two sections up vertically to less than 10ft for travelling on the road. At the Royal Show in 1969 they won a RASE Silver Award for this innovation. They also won awards from the Scottish Agricultural Association.

The earlier MK II was also sold with a Perkins 6.354 Diesel engine giving 105hp, with optional Turbo version, the T6.354 giving 135hp. It had a ZF gearbox, 4 forward and 1 reverse gearbox with a traction variator fitted. Later MK II models were modified with the power unit changing to Ford, a N/A 2715E engine, of 105hp or optional Turbocharged 2507ET engine, of 135hp. The shaker shoe in later MK II models was changed, and larger grain tank fitted. Colour scheme changed from the all blue with red wheels to white and blue.

This MARK III Lely Victory with 14ft header dates from 1979, and belongs to Mr Glyn Hughes of Denbigh North Wales. Here his son Emyr Hughes is cutting spring barley. It still does contract cutting 150 acres a year in the neighbourhood, for stock rearing farmers, and was previously used as part of a fleet of three on a farm in Hampshire.

This combine is a later model with blue and white colour scheme. The power came from a Ford 2715E 6 cylinder 108hp diesel engine, a Ford 135hp type 270ET turbo charged engine was an option. The Cab Craft cab was on the combine when new, offered as an extra which also had an Air conditioning blower unit, which has since been removed.

The MK III joined the existing MK II later, it had an identical threshing mechanism to the MK II model, with 54ins wide drum, but the Traction variator was replaced by the Linde Hydrostatic Unit, one of the first hydrostatic combines available at the time. The Mark III had hydrostatic transmission as standard, instead of manual transmission on the Mark II version. The fuel tank held 70 gallons.

The folding header is unique to Lely. It was simple to operate, to activate it, all that was needed was to push a lever, the table would hydraulically unfold, after inserting a locking pin, the combine was ready for work. It has advanced hydrostatic steering and hydraulic controls, reel speed was hydraulically adjustable, as was the up and down fore and aft. Table flotation was by means of a compressed nitrogen cylinder, which made the table responsive to ground pressure. The Mark II and III were offered with a 14ft or 18ft header, which folded, each half being driven by its own hydraulic motor which was interconnected with the other for identical speed balance, with speed being adjustable from the platform. The reel fore and aft and up and down was hydraulically controlled.

Other innovations were micro switches being fitted for the straw walkers and Grain elevator drives, giving warning lights on the steering column warning the driver of any blockages. They were a high capacity machine with an extra large shaker shoe and sieve pan and five large straw walkers. The grain tank held 100 bushels or 3637 litres. With a transport width of 9ft 6in and an output of up to 17 tons an hour, they had five straw walkers and a large 23.5in diameter drum. The Mark III with 18ft cut table cost £27,888 in 1980, and it was sold alongside the Mark II which was priced at £23,253 with 18ft cut table. The cab complete with air filtration fan and electric wiper was £1,071, plus £1,092 for the larger engine.

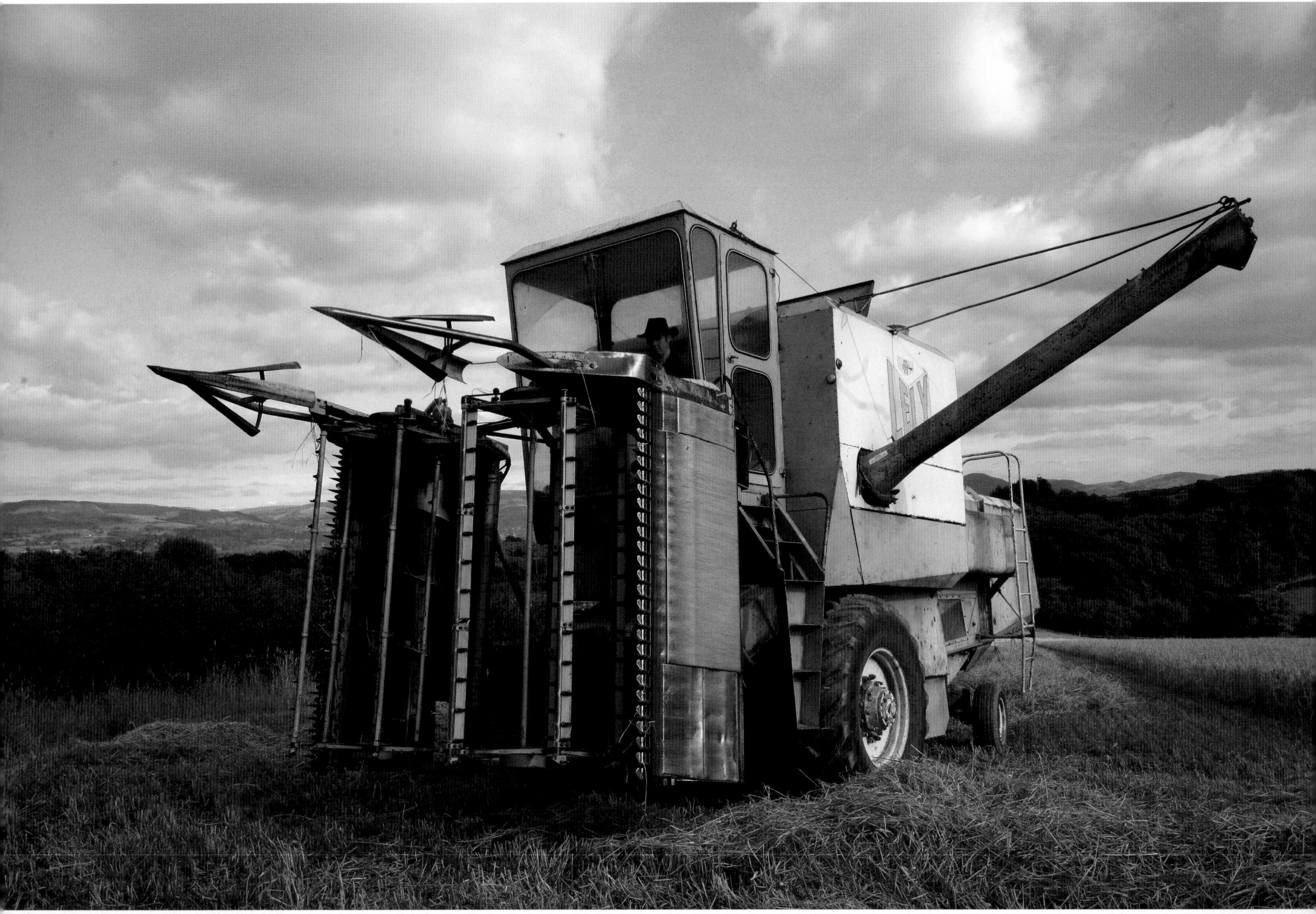
LELY

FORTSCHRITT

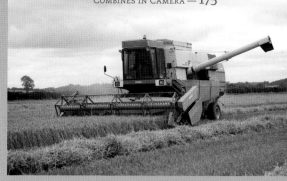

Fortschritt of East Germany had already been exporting combines to the UK for 15 years, when a report was undertaken on these combines in 1989. These were considered unsophisticated up against their Western rivals, but they were very much cheaper in price. In spite of this, they were featured with an automatic lateral and fore and aft table levelling system for twelve years prior to 1989, by which time some western manufacturers had only just brought this feature to a manual version. At this time, the E517 was the top of the range model. In the mid 1980's, they had been imported by Burgess. A farmer in Warwickshire in 1989 had harvested on average 120 tonnes in an eight hour day, he had an E516 prior to this machine.

In 1989, Bonhill Engineering importers of Fortschritt combines, by then operating from Brough, North Humberside, handled three models, the E514, E517, E524 and E516 were still in the fields. They were all non rotary with a wobble box knife drive with conventional drum and concave. They had levers for the travel direction, speed and reel and table functions, apart from the E524 which had a joystick. They were all fitted with an on board computer which gave information on grain losses, area harvested, harvesting time and travel speed. The E516, 517 and E524 had auto lateral and fore and aft levelling system, so that the table was free to follow ground contours independently of the wheels. Lateral compensation was by springs whose tension was preset.

E517

This E517 with a 19ft header is twenty two years old at the time of writing. It belongs to Ken Hutsby near Stratford upon Avon, and is working in wheat at Staple Hill Farm, Wellsbourne, Warwickshire. This combine still cuts around 400 acres of wheat a year. It is a useful machine on this farm because it leaves longer straw which is suitable for baling in conventional small bales for sale to race horse owners, whereas modern combines leave a shorter straw less suitable for this purpose. It works alongside a Lexion 570C which cuts the remainder of the wheat and OSR.

The five straw walker E517 model was marketed in the 1980's. It was available in cutting widths of 5.70m and 6.70m with grain lifters and dividers offered as standard. The fore and aft flotation on the 517 was controlled by springs which were preset, but could be over ridden hydraulically from the cab. It has an 800mm drum diameter and width of 1625mm. Transmission was hydrostatic. The cab had laminated glass, onboard computer, performance monitors and hectare counter as standard, but air conditioning was optional. The grain

tank had a capacity of 5.5cm. Powered by a V8 diesel engine of 168hp, they were considered a high output combine in their day. The E517 had generous separating and cleaning areas, which included a three stage triple cascade cleaning system with high output fan, which blew air over the top two sieves. A re-thresher handled the returns which were passed to the grain pan rather than to the drum. A Rekord straw chopper was an optional extra. Weight with 7.60m cutter bar was 2030kg.

— **Below**

E412 left in corner of a field awaiting collection by foreign buyer for export. This was a smaller model, the earlier livery of Fortschritt combines was blue, before the livery changed to green.

— This Page

Bonhill E517 and Lexion 570C, working together at Wellsbourne, Stratford Upon Avon, Warwickshire. Belonging to Ken Hutsby of Thornton Manor, Ettington.

Part 2

Plot Combines

Trials Equipment (UK) Ltd now imports trials machinery to the UK markets. They first started converting combines for the trials industry in 1986.

These plot combines are used at the Institute of Biological Environmental and Rural Sciences at Aberystwyth University at Plas Gogerddan, Aberystwyth, to harvest 4 metre crop trials of mainly grass seed, perennial rye grass red and white clover which is grown for commercial use in agriculture and oats.

HEGE 125 & 140

Made in Germany, Hege was bought by the Austrian Company Wintersteiger in the late 1990's.

Hege started a new period of mechanisation of research work all over the world and the 125 was followed by the higher capacity 125B, which had more engine power.

The 125 was especially suited for threshing small plots in research work. It runs clean in a few seconds and is suitable for all cereals, as well as soy beans, legume seeds, grass seeds, oil seeds and many others. It has an open design beater type drum, so that it gives a free view to the concave. The cutting height and reel position are hydraulically controlled. A transverse turbine fan gives an equal airstream through the cleaning sieve.The Drum width is 800mm with 6 rasp bars and the combine has one shaker.

Both these combines are available with header widths of 1.25m and 1.50m. The 125 B was powered by a VW 38hp engine.

HEGE 140

Available in cutting widths of 1.25m to 3m headers have a intake auger behind which is a feeding roller to evenly transport the material to the threshing drum. It has a variable speed drum adjustable from driver's seat, and two step straw shaker, A conveyor band takes the threshed crop to the sieve system. An optional grain tank has a capacity of 600 litres. Seed is conveyed by pneumatic means to the seed hopper. It is available with either the Grain Gage Harvest Master weighing system which has a control and conditioning unit, printer and hand held computer, or the weighing system originally developed at Hege for seed breeding. The control unit evaluates, displays the signals of the weighing cells and prints them Out on a printer. At the same time, the Control Unit controls the opening and closing of the flaps of the weighing container. With the standard weighing system the data is read off a paper strip and manually entered into a computer. An automatic version uses a system where the data collection device on the combine is connected with the control unit. The weight data is automatically entered into the trial plans while harvesting, and transferred to the station computer when harvesting is finished.

WINTERSTEIGER NURSERY MASTER 1300 HYDRO

Supplied and marketed by Trials Equipment (UK) Ltd of Braintree Essex, the Nurserymaster was introduced in 1978, to follow on from the Seedmaster 125 and Seedmaster Universal. This has an especially compact constructional form, is light weight and with its optimal self cleaning, prevented the crop getting mixed. It is a 4ft bagger plot combine powered by VW 1600CC engine, They were later powered by a 1900cc engine. It was sold alongside the older and more tested Seedmaster Universal. The newer Nurserymaster which was fully hydrostatic, was designed for smaller plants, and for firms where there are experimental plants in different places, as these machines could be easily transported on a car trailer.

An earlier Nurserymaster hydrostatic model was driven by a VW Industrial engine of 30hp 1200ccm engine, it had a 125cm cut and was a gearless hydrostatic drive combine, with hydraulic lifting of the table and reel. The drum width was 800mm and diameter 250mm with six rasp bars and one shaker. Like conventional combines, the concave could be adjusted at the front and rear and it had four drum speeds. The Nurserymaster had a cross mounted cleaning system which blows air over the whole sieve width and a wind blower for cleaning of the threshing unit at the plot ends is adjustable from the driver's seat.

The grain in the three Wintersteiger combines is blown into a hopper and bagged off.

The Nursery Master Elite model was marketed from 1989 to 2001, when it was replaced by the Classic model.

Wintersteiger based in Austria are the premier supplier of trials machinery in the world, and manufacture seeders, forage plot harvesters, laboratory equipment as well as combines. Wintersteiger has been engaged in the production of special plant breeding machinery since 1954, and in 1968, they were the first firm in the world to start the assembly line production of special combine harvesters.

WINTERSTEIGER CLASSIC

New in 2008, has 1.2 metre cut powered by water cooled VW Golf diesel engine 38kW 52 continental hp.1900cc.

It is available in header widths of 124 cm 4ft or 150cm 5ft, with a Uniflow header, which is a combination of an intake auger, transfer drum and conveyor belt. Thre is an emergency stop feature for the header reel and conveyor belt.

It has hydrostatic transmission, and electro hydraulically controlled differential lock. A useful feature is a compressor with air hose for cleaning the combine. A multi functional lever controls driving and harvesting functions, header and reel functions, differential lock on or off, weighing system at end of the plot and transmission forward and reverse. Threshing is with a drum size of 14in diameter and 31in wide, and 8 bar concave, the drum speed is changed by a variator.

It has two shaker lengths, eight cleaning sieve sizes from 4 to 24 and 28mm for different crops and fan with speed range from 650 to 1500rpm.

There are three options for grain collection, grain can be bagged off from the left hand side, this is a pneumatic 2 person harvesting procedure, with adjustable blower and double bag holder. On the right hand side, top mounted bagging can be undertaken beside the driver with a pneumatic conveyor system. The 250 or 400 litre grain tank with pneumatic filling and discharge auger can be used for trailer filling. The discharge auger is driven hydraulically.

Measurement sensors in the optional Wintersteiger weighing system records plot weight, moisture content, and volumatic weight, the logged harvest data is stored on the electronic hand held pc,

and printed out on the field printer.

Optional extras for the header include grain lifters, two brushes on the reel to clean the cutter bar, extra long crop dividers, vertical cutter bar on right or left of header for rape and a pick up device for harvesting swathed crops.

WINTERSTEIGER SEEDMASTER

There were several Seedmaster models. One was powered by VW 38hp engine, the combine was made for crops of bigger plots and increasing areas with cutting widths of 150 and 175cm.

THE SEEDMASTER UNIVERSAL

This model evolved from the Seedmaster 125. Its hydrostatic drive enables it to drive in a nursery. A powerful blowing system cleans, within seconds, the whole combine from the front table back to the straw discharge hood. Flexible covers on every connection part within the combine prevent mixing of seed losses. A gearless and adjustable wind blower gives a super cleaning effect. This enables threshing of cereals, beans, clover and most grass and vegetable seeds. It was available with tables of 125, 150 and 175cm widths. The drum width was 800mm diameter 350mm with six rasp bars and one shaker, and powered by a VW Industrial 29hp engine.

SAMPO ROSENLEW 2010

Sampo produce the 2010 plot combine which has established itself in the UK as the leading plot combine, and has added the larger 2035 Plot combine to their range. They have also made plot combines for MF in the past, including the Number 8 Plot combine and 10.

Sampo produce the 2010 Plot combine which has become the leading trials combine in the UK. With cab, the latest plot combine has unloading auger, the reel has plastic tines. This Sampo combine with 2 metre header and three straw walkers also has a chute in the cab to bag off a sample. The cab is wide enough for space for a seat for the technician, where the weighing controls can be operated. It has a computer with a database, the seed is blown into a weigh hopper and the computer will weigh the sample, a switch on the control console enables grain to be tanked or bagged off. It has hydrostatic transmission, with infinitely variable drive speed, and has been designed based on an earlier MF plot combine made in Denmark. The computer weighs, records moisture and hectometre and can print it out on a PC card. A feature of this combine is the CHAC System, Constant High Airstream Cleaning, which generated a continuous air stream of the entire cutting table, to avoid contamination. This plot combine cost £73,000 five years ago. It is available with 1.5m, 2.0m and 3.0m headers and powered by a 82hp 4 cylinder diesel

engine. The grain tank holds 1700 litres. The Sampo 2010 is offered with a bagging system and straw chopper as options. The combine can be equipped with either the Grain gage weighing system from Wintersteiger, or a Coleman weighing system produced by Trials Equipment. This is pneumatically operated and is calibrated to within 50g. Grain is transported via a conveyor and chute under the elevator to a weigh hopper on the right hand side of the cab. After weighing the grain is transported across the combine using the cleaning blower, while the next plot is being harvested. The blower automatically changes back to cleaning the combine after the grain has finished transferring across the combine. It is also available with maize sunflower headers and OSR extensions.

There is also a larger 2035 plot combine, which is equipped with air cleaning and can have either of two weighing systems fitted.

— **Left**

Sampo Rosenlew 2010 AT NIAB - National Institute of Agricultural Botany farm on

Duchy of Cornwall Estate, at Monkhall Callow Hereford.

This Plot combine cuts 4,000 plots over 20 acres of mainly wheat and oilseed rape, but also beans peas and barley. This plot combine can harvest 40 plots an hour, which are 12m by 2m in size.

— **Below Left**

Sampo Rosenlew 2010 plot combine, Institute of Biological Environmental and Rural Sciences at Aberystwyth University, Plas Gogerddan, Aberystwyth.

— **Below**

Straw Chopper On Sampo 2010 plot Combine At NIAB Monkhall Callow Hereford.

Two small combines adapted for use as plot combines.

DEUTZ FAHR FARM LINER 3370

This has a 6ft header, powered by 80hp Deutz air cooled engine, it dates from the 1990's.

This combine is still used as a plot combine at the Institute of Biological Environmental and Rural Sciences, Aberystwyth University at Plas Gogerddan, Aberystwyth. With its narrow 6ft header, it is convenient for cutting the narrow 4 meter plots of trial seeds. It is powered by a Deutz 80hp engine.

CLAAS COMPACT 25

Used at The Institute of Biological Environmental and Rural Sciences at Aberystwyth University.

John Deere factory Zweibrucken Germany

— **BELOW**
Combine increases in size as it travels down the assembly line.

— **BOTTOM LEFT**
Another stage of the assembly line.

The factory only uses paints which are lead free, chromium and zinc for combine bodies, also JD dip their machines unlike most other manufacturers who paint the individual parts prior to assembly.

The advanced E coat paint facility at Zweibrucken is a good example of the company's commitment to quality and ranks as the most modern of its kind in Europe.

The large combine modules are assembled first, before being painted using a newly-developed epoxy material that triples corrosion protection, compared with the previously used conventional spray and dip paints. The assembled machine body is moved through a series of tanks, immersing it completely to clean and treat every metal surface for a strong permanent bonds the machine is painted. As it lowers into the paint electric current charge. The bath carriesthe opposite charge, with the result that the paint is magnetically attracted to every metal surface. About 80 kilo of paint including the primary and final coast is applied to each combine.

— **BELOW RIGHT**
End of th assembly line at Zweibrucken. Another high output combine rolls off the assembly line and is ready for despatch to the dealer.

— **BOTTOM CENTRE**
Paint area.

— **Right**

One of the latest T670i combines out on the demonstration track.

— **Below Right**

C 670i in the showroom at the John Deere combine factory in Zweibrucken Germany.

'Nothing runs like a Deere' is the trademark of the John Deere Company and this symbolises the heritage of past achievements and is poised for new innovations to come. For every slice of bread eaten in the world, 42 per cent, of the grain is harvested by a John Deere combine. This makes John Deere the world's largest manufacturer of combine harvesters with an average annual production that is between two and three times more than each of its major competitors.

Training

Companies today require highly trained technicians to service modern combines, and all companies guarantee regular ongoing training to keep Service Engineers up to date with increasing technical aspects of modern machinery.

— OPPOSITE PAGE

CLAAS Academy At Saxham at CLAAS UK. CLAAS UK is the Marketing and Sales UK headquarters for CLAAS in Britain and is responsible for distribution of all CLAAS combines, parts and other machinery in England, Scotland and Wales. In addition, there are two Harvest Centres, one in Bury St Edmunds and one in Edinburgh. The CLAAS dealer network covers the entire country with 80 outlets specialising in all CLAAS machinery, with certain key dealers specialising in harvest equipment. Dealers are trained to consult closely on every new combine purchased, matched to a MAXICARE Service contract in many cases with parts support.

Modern agriculture relies increasingly on fewer higher capacity machines. To ensure that dealers have access to skilled technicians that are now required, Agricultural Technician apprenticeship schemes are operated. Staff from dealerships can also attain in house qualifications and status, for example Master Mechanic and Master technician awards.

With the advances in electronics on modern combines, technicians need to be highly trained. The CLAAS Academy was opened in 2003 and is the centre for training combine operators and dealer service personnel and is where technical courses are held. The CLAAS Academy aims to ensure that everyone associated with the machines has access to the necessary training, in order that the full potential of modern combines is realised.

— RIGHT

Training room at the training centre at Zedelgem, operators and dealers are trained in the technical features of the new CR9090 combine.

— ABOVE RIGHT

CR9090 in training room at Zedelgem Belgium.

— RIGHT

John Deere marketing headquarters at Langar, Nottinghamshire, UK.

Dealers are linked to Langar for back up service and parts supply. The parts centre from Langar can take and process orders from the dealer up to 7pm every weekday in season and at weekends at an earlier cut off time. Parts are picked and all but the largest placed in individual dealer containers using electronic bar coding to eliminate errors. Dedicated delivery vehicles deliver the parts in returnable environmentally friendly shipping containers.

Dealerships

New combines are sold through appointed dealerships. A family dealership who has sold Claas combines for fifty years is Morris Corfield & Co in Shropshire.

— **BELOW**

The founder on the right and two of the first salesmen and son of founder stand by a Claas SF.

— **BELOW CENTRE**

By Lexion 580+. The founders of a well known family dealership in combines based in Shropshire covering the West Midlands and North Wales areas.

Morris Corfield & Co George Pugh /John Corfield History

John Corfield, now in his early eighties started at Craven Arms in the late 1950s, around 1959 to 1960, in those days he was the manager and salesman. George Pugh started in November 1959 and together with John Corfield became the team, and retired in 1990. George Pugh has seen many changes in combines during his career as a salesman.

John Morris' Father Leslie P Morris started at Craven Arms and had worked for Bromleys of Wellington in a blacksmith shop during the war. He became based at Craven Arms and also ran Morris Bufton based at Ludlow. Les offered John Corfield a partnership in the firm, so it became Morris Corfield as it is still known today.

One of the first combines sold was probably a trailed Claas Super Automatic in 1962 which went to Pitchford. The first self propelled combine sold was a Claas SF, to Milner Whiteman, Arscott farm, Posenhall, Shropshire. George sold this to Forresters of Willey Farm Benthal, in 1963 for the 1964 season, then to Jo Rowson, Cleobury North. George Green of Cleobury North, his son-in-law bought this SF for £200 in 1969, when his Father in Law had a farm sale. George Green had been driving this combine. Just after the purchase, two people asked if George would continue to do their combining for them, so the SF carried on cutting about 200 acres until it was replaced by a Senator, which was also bought at a sale. The SF then came to the dealer's yard at Benthal, because it was one of the first John Corfield sold.

The combine trade really took off in 1964 with the advent of the Matador. A local farmer Geoff Jones of Brockton Farm had three 726 combines, but during harvest only one of them was going. A demonstrator, a Matador Giant was on tour and had done some acres before it arrived at Brockton where it did 50 acres the second day there, quite an achievement in those days. This combine became one of the biggest sellers of all time, at one time, George recalls there were 37 second hand machines in the yard!

George says that they sold combines to three different agricultural contractors, Hawkins of Lobbington in Wem, Warners and Phil Pinches, who helped George to find sales outlets for the Claas Combines.

The news soon spread about how well the Matador had performed at Geoff Jones farm. It was this demonstration and the Giant Matador which really got the firm going in the combine market. Soon they were taking back Massey Ferguson 780 combines and a few Claysons and earlier trailer machines. The 780s and the successor the 788, had been the king of the harvest fields for some time, but when the Matador appeared, they could not keep up with it. In those days, George says that most combines taken in part exchange were sold again as retail, whereas now, many go for export.

In the early days, not many of the other Claas combines were sold, only two Europas, a few Mercurys, and none of the Columbus models, these were too small for the average farmers requirements. The Matador and the Giant Matador and Matador Standard which followed were the best sellers, around 1965, 30 Matadors were sold in one year, more of these were sold than any other machine.

In the late 1960s, the Mercator was launched, but this machine was not a big success, it was a wet harvest that year George recalls, around 1968 and the concaves were blocking from damp straw, they had to be modified with wider concaves. The name changed to Senator, in order to have a fresh name on the machine after the disappointing performance of the Mercator. Claas had

lifters on all their combines, whereas other manufactures did not, this gave them a lead in the market at this time. The crop could be lifted into the header better. The Claas combine had been tested in the Polder region of Holland in damper conditions. George recalls that Claas always backed them well, and the Germans often came over to see machines working. Claas was the best firm to deal with in those days and they never argued about warranty or if a machine was not working right. George had worked with an International dealer in 1954 when the trailer models were sold, but even from the early days, Claas combines would go where other machines couldn't.

Of course there were some models which were not so popular. The Dominator 100's gave trouble, as George says, due to a change to sealed bearings at this time. In the early days, all the bearings were grease bearings, then these changed to sealed ones, and also the price started to rise in the early 1980's. Up until then, combine prices had remained fairly static. In 1964, a Standard Matador retailed at £2,200 and a Matador Giant £2,800.

There were numerous combine dealers in the 1960's and 1970's, in Shropshire, Reginald Tildsey who were once Claas dealers and also held a franchise for New Holland sold a few machines, but none to the extent of the Morris Corfield concern.

— **Left**

John Morris opens the new premises at Benthall Broseley Shropshire. The family owned firm celebrated 50 years of trading in April 2010.

Mill Engineers of Ablingdon, Oxfordshire are supported by the Claas Group, supplying combines to farms in the counties of Worcestershire, Warwickshire, Gloucestershire and Wiltshire as well as parts of Oxfordshire. The business merged with Vaughan Agri in 2002 to create Western Harvesters. The firm was founded in 1955 and in the late nineties the business expanded from its long established base at Bibury near Cirencester to open a new base near Pewsey, near Marlborough . In 2004, the firm relocated its Evesham operations to Shipston on Stour. They are also members of Combine World.

— **ABOVE**
Row of headers await sale in dealers yard Mill Engineers at Ablington Gloucestershire.

— **LEFT**
Row of Lexion Combines await new owners.

STORY OF J MANN & SONS

Another established dealership is - J Mann & Sons of Saxham, a division of Anglia Harvesters, which serves farmers in East Anglia, for distribution of Claas combines, who first imported Claas combines into Britain.

J MANN OF SAXHAM

This firm is worth a mention as they were the first to sell Claas combines in the UK, when they became Claas distributers in 1947 and imported 11 Claas Super Junior combines to Britain.

There has been a close link between Claas and Manns for many years. Manns is one of five daughter companies within the Claas Group.

The arrival of Claas in the UK dates back to July 1946 when Lord Walston visited a German farm to assess a Claas combine

working and returned with a favourable report.

Just after the war, in 1946, a combine harvester in the Claas factory was confiscated and shipped to Askham Bryan in Yorkshire, where it was evaluated at the MIAE Member of the Institution of

Automobile Engineers. Dr Brenner from Claas, who designed it, was also sent to monitor its performance. An English intelligence officer who was a custodian of enemy property confiscated 11 Claas combines which he offered to various manufacturers in England, including Ransomes, but no one was interested.

Larant of Watford, who had imported Claas balers from 1936 to 1939 was approached about taking the combines, to which they agreed, but were unable to pay for them. The eleven combines had already shipped from the Claas factory to the docks at Hamburg, so the Board of Trade were left with the machines at the docks with nowhere to go. Manns associations date back to 1929, when they were agents for Lanz tractors. Bill Mann had a small engineering business in Saxham near Bury St Edmunds. James Mann, who farmed at Saxham had taken on the agency for Lanz tractors and was joined in business by his son, also James, but known as Bill in 1934. Bill was the main force behind the combine venture.

Bill Mann ordered some parts for the Lanz Bulldog tractors he was importing from Germany. The Board of Trade had to approve this transaction. As a result of this Bill Mann was contacted by Roy Wieck, who by now had moved to the Board after returning from Germany as the intelligence officer who confiscated the combines. Bill Mann agreed to purchase the combines after consulting the MIAE in Yorkshire where they had been on test. The combines were shipped to the docks at Tilbury.

Another 50 Claas combines were available after the 1947 harvest. The Board of Trade summoned three dealers, Bill Mann, Larant of Watford and Lenfields of Maidstone to a meeting to decide future imports of Claas combines.

Bill Mann sold most of the combines allocated to Larant and Lenfield as well as his quota of 17, out of the 50 machines.

After the 1948 Harvest the Board of Trade decided that having three importers was unsatisfactory, so August Claas who was present was given the casting vote. As a result, Bill Mann who was the choice became J Mann and Sons and subsequently became the sole importers of Claas Machinery to the UK in 1948.

Roy Wieck who was multilingual, became the liaison office between Claas and Manns, arranging sales promotions, translations and shipping. In 1949, Manns became a limited company trading as J Mann and Son Ltd, more commonly known as Manns of Saxham. Bill Mann sold the company to Howard Machinery in 1969, but the name was retained and they continued as sole Claas importer for the UK. The agreement for Claas to buy Manns from Howard machinery Ltd was confirmed in 1990, just before the Smithfield Show, but Manns continued to represent the Claas franchise in the arable area of East Anglia and is associated with the family that originally imported Claas combines into the UK back in 1947,while Claas UK became established as the importer.

In 1980, a daughter marketing company was established at Saxham, Bury St Edmunds, known as Claas UK.

Manns imported 500 Super combines for the 1949/50 harvests. 220 trailed Claas combines had been sold in 1949. Manns brought in 13 of the SF combines for the 1953 harvest. The SF was introduced at the Royal Show, held in Blackpoo,l priced at £2,300.

J Mann and Son was formed in its present style in 1989. It is situated close to Combine World.

— OPPOSITE PAGE
Combines in combine world store at Saxham await sale.

— LEFT
J Mann and Sons were co founders of Combine World, which specialises in used combines. Many Claas and other combines are sold through Combine World, second hand. Combine World was formed in 1989, it comprises sixteen dealers and is a specialist in used combines and is based next to Claas UK and Manns of Saxham in Suffolk. Every combine sold carries a 165 point inspection report detailing all the service work which is required. In addition, selected machines will have all this work completed so that they are ready for harvest, together with Combine World Warranty. Since its formation, over 3,500 combines with a value of over £100 million have been sold.

ALEXANDER AND DUNCAN

Alexander and Duncan is an independent dealership for John Deere combines, supplying the Midlands area.

The firm dates back to 1855 when Samuel Alexander an Ironmonger from a Quaker family started an ironmongery and agricultural machinery business in Leominster. The firm later became the leading agricultural engineering company in Herefordshire. As Alexander and Loveridge, following the formation of a new partnership when Thomas Loveridge joined in the mid 1800's, the company sold fire grates and open ranges, a variety of reapers and mowers, harrows ploughs and other implements and galvanised cattle troughs. An apprentice who had joined the business, Andrew Thomas Duncan was later to take charge of the business. Soon after the death of Samuel Alexander in 1884, and the departure of Thomas Loveridge from the business a new partnership of the founder's son, Samuel Joseph Alexander and Andrew Duncan was formed, during which time the business expanded with the erection of French barns.

By the twentieth century, the development of the internal combustion engine and its application to agriculture was to bring about major changes in farm machinery. The company exhibited oil engines at local shows, which had appeared in the 1890s and were used as stationery engines to drive chaff cutters and other barn machinery. As the mechanisation of agriculture increased, the manufacture and supply of agricultural machinery including increasingly large combine harvesters and tractors was expanding rapidly. This in turn led to a decision by the company to sell off the barn business. The ironmongery side of the business like many others at this time came under pressure from supermarkets selling pre packaged hardware items. Sale of machinery therefore took the place of the erection of barns and the ironmongery business. By 1975 they moved to new premises in Leominster where the company remains today, following a management buy-out in 1984. Cyril Amos had been an apprentice with the company and is now Managing Director. His son Simon is now in charge of the main sales department. Alexander and Duncan was the seventh firm in the UK to sign up with John Deere when they took on the John Deere franchise in 1966 and became one of the main John Deere dealers in the West Midlands. The firm founded over a hundred years ago by Samuel Alexander is now the leading John Deere supplier of combines and tractors in the region.

— **BELOW**
A new combine arrives at Alexander and Duncan, Leominster, Herefordshire.

— **BOTTOM**
Combine in dealers yard at Alexander and Duncan awaits a purchaser.

— **This Page**

Lexion 570+Montana works into the night, for manager Shaun Watson of John Davies Farms, Swancote, Bridgnorth, Shropshire. Farmer and contractor John Fox cuts Castille OSR.

Night Time operations

— **BELOW**
CR 960 in OSR at dusk as sun goes down near Madley Herefordshire. This combine cuts a large acreage for a potato and cereal grower near Vowchurch, Herefordshire.

Lexion 570+ Montana in wheat at John Davies Farms, Swancote, Bridgnorth, Shropshire.

These days harvest often continues on into the night, sometimes around the clock and with a change of drivers, in unsettled weather. Lexion combines according to the model, have powerful front facing Xenon headlights which turn night into day as well as Stubble lights, front axle lights, Side Finder lights and rear reversing lights.

— **Right**

Lexion 510 at Edward and Andrew Quicks Farm at Thurloxton near Taunton in Somerset unloading at night.

— **Main Image**

Lexion 470 cutting N K Grace OSR with Ragleth hills in the background, for Mr Edward Jones at Acton Scott farm, Church Stretton, Shropshire. It belongs to contractor Neil Morris of Nash near Ludlow who covers a wide area contracting in Shropshire.

198 — Combines in Camera

— **Main Image**

Lexion 530 Montana, Withypool Farm,
Cleaobury Mortimer.

— **Inset**

Lexion 480 at Little Stepple Farm,
Cleobury Mortimer.

Transport

— **RIGHT**

Lexion 570+ arrives at a farm near Craven Arms, Shropshire, on truck from the hauliers yard.

Richard Long Ltd are hauliers for Claas machinery in the UK. Here a truck driven by Billy arrives with a new combine at a farm in Shropshire, bought through Shropshire Claas dealers Morris Corfield & Co.

Machines are transported by truck from the factory at Harsewinkel in Germany, with the wheels removed, because of limits on the width of transporting wide loads to The Hook of Holland or Europort, from where they go by ferry to Harwich port. From there they are sent by truck to the depot at Richard Long, Norwich where the wheels are put on and despatched to the dealers in the UK.

Combines have got much larger in recent years, and moving them from field to field is an important consideration, especially for contractors. On today's machines, the headers are all detachable, enabling the width of the machine to be reduced and transported either separately or towed behind the combine.

John Deere transport

A new combine arrives at Alexander and Duncan, John Deere dealers of Leominster ,Herefordshire.

— **BELOW**

W Coy & Son of Langar John Deere transport deliver a new T560 combine to Alexander and Duncan, Leominster, Herefordshire.

— **Left**
New Lexion arrives on low loader to Morris Corfield & Co Ltd, Shropshire where it will have PDI test before being driven to the farm.

— **Below**
Leaving Zedelgem factory, Belgium on truck.

— **Below**

Mercedes Unimog transports V1200 header off a Lexion 600 on Claas road tour Wiltshire.

— **Right**

A new Lexion 570+ and header arrives at farm from the dealers.

Workshop Scenes

— LEFT

View under the panel of modern combine. This 580+ undergoes a complete ovrerhaul after the tough harvest condtions of 2008.

— CENTRE LEFT

APS drum removed.

— BELOW LEFT

The main drum is replaced after repair from stone damage.

— BELOW

Lexion 540 in workshop at Morris Corfields new workshops at Benthall Broseley, Shropshire undergoes repair and servicing before resale.

— **LEFT**
Ravenhill of Hereford. A new CX 8060 in workshop for PDI check before delivery. This CX8060 has extra large tyres front size 1050 rear 800's

— **BELOW LEFT**
Two Lexion 580+ combines at Morris Corfield, Benthall, Broseley, Shropshire.

Parts of combine being repaired at Morris Corfield & Co Ltd. workshop.

— **BELOW**

Drums and concaves are often in need of repair in the workshop.

— **BELOW RIGHT**

View inside combine with drums removed. Concaves and drums. The APS drum is replaced after the repaired drum and concaves are put back.

— **TOP RIGHT**

Damaged and bent concaves from stones are repaired.

— **RIGHT CENTRE**

A four wheel drive axle is fitted to a Lexion.

A common job in the workshop is repairing or straightening damaged and bent rasp bars on the drum, or completely replacing them. After the wet harvests of 2007 and 2008, there were many damaged and bent drums in combines from stones entering, due to the driver having to cut very low to salvage lodged crops in wet conditions.

Concaves also have to be straightened, making it necessary for the drums and concaves to be removed from the machine.

A 4 wheel drive back axle is put on a Lexion 580+ at Morris Corfield and Co Ltd. in workshop, Benthall, Broseley, Shropshire.

A four wheel drive axle is put on this Lexion 580+ instead of a two wheel drive axle, many four wheel drive kits have been sold since the very wet conditions of harvest 2007, some farmers had a four wheel drive kit installed replacing the two wheel drive axle on their combines.

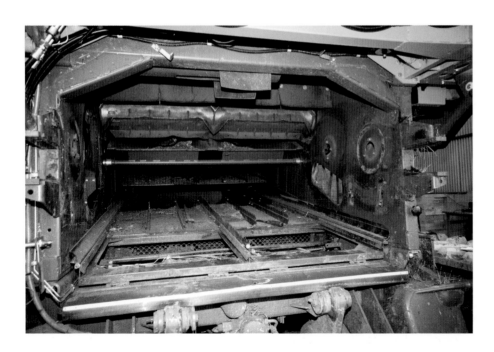

Servicing and Maintenance

— RIGHT

This Lexion 470 at J G Goring Ltd, Hereford is an example of a well maintained combine, here in between the dry spells the radiator is cleaned on a regular basis.

Maintenance in the field on this 470 between dry spells, blowing off the rotary radiator screen and other parts with compressed air.

PDI CHECKS AND SERVICNG

During servicing, some of the main areas covered are checking that the gearbox levels are correct, checking for worn bearings, correct tension of roller chains, checking V belts for wear. Elevator chains, for example the returns elevator chain and drive belts and chains are tensioned. Variable speed pulleys checked and greased, general lubrication of the machine. Hydraulic system and hoses checked for leaks, hydraulic oil changed, engine oil and for fuel hydraulic and air filters changed. Oil in the threshing drum reduction gearbox is changed.

Wearing parts such as knives retracting tines on intake auger are checked, chains and belts adjusted, straw walker bearings, any other bearings such as drum bearings,

the electrics and warning lights checked. Lubrication points such as the grain tank unloading gearbox and lubricating pump for the grain tank unloading mechanism are checked,

— RIGHT

Lexion and PDI checks. Combine technician Dave Harris does a PDI check at dealership at Morris Corfield and Co Ltd at Docklow, Leominster, Herefordshire on a new Lexion before despatch to farm.

Pre delivery work of all new combines to the farm, involves:

• Check engine oil level
• Coolant level
• Air filter seating and air filter cartridge
• Check on rotary screen and drive belt
• Check for transport damage- guards, chassis, wheel rims etc
• Remove any transport clamps for the cab roof, and securing wires from unloading auger and guards, steps etc
• Remove components from inside of grain tank stored for transport
• Mirrors and accessories, fire extinguishers radio aerial fitted
• Tracking is checked

• Pivoting steering axle, remove stop bolts
• Rear axle changed from transport to working position
• Oil levels in gearboxes,
  1. Main gearbox behind front drive shaft
  2. Reduction gear boxes-where wheels bolted to
  3. Two gear boxes for the rotors
  4. Transfer gear box on the engine
• Oil levels on the header
  1. Rape knife drive on left of header at the back
  2. Wobble box oil level
• Auger extension plates in centre, which narrows the space for the intake of crop to feeder housing, removed.
• Transmission wheels brakes
  1. Nuts and bolts etc checked
  2. Brake fluid level
• Engine
  1. Coolant levels and condition
  2. Air intake pipe, checked tightened if necessary
  3. Check fuel tank level
• Gearboxes/Drive/Hydraulics/Electrics
• Hydraulic system and engine coolant checked for leaks
• Battery charge level checked
• Auto Contour working
• Concave settings set as for factory setting from which any adjustments are taken

• Grain tank Sensors and warning beacon outside cab-check working, these show when tank is half and three quarters and full on Cebis display)
• Main Bearings greased

Combinable Crops

The term combinable crops appeared during the 1980's, and referred to any crops that could be harvested with a combine harvester. Aside from wheat, barley and oats, it includes sunflowers, oil seed rape, lupins, linseed, beans, peas, buckwheat and millet.

Lexion 430 cuts sunflowers for Mr Patrick Wrixon at Devereux Wootton Farm, Norton Canon, Herefordshire, where the seeds are sent locally for sale as bird seed. These are grown for their seeds, which are sold in health foods and the seeds are also sold in pet shops for small rodents. At

Devereux Wootton, Mr Patrick Wrixon has sold seed produced on his farm, which is a member of LEAF (Linking Environment and Farming), an organisation founded in the early 1990's, whereby in addition to producing food, farmers could improve their natural habitats through integrated

farm management. Seed is used for making bird seed mixtures for commercial use though a third party. Animal feed can be made from a by product of the seeds after the oil is extracted. The oil is beneficial in cooking, being low in unsaturated fats.

GRASS SEED

— Below Right

Lexion 530 Montana with Shelbourne Reynolds header in grass seed at Withypool Farm near Cleobury Mortimer, Worcesterhire.

— Right

MF 40 in grass seed at Bowling Green Farm near Madley, Herefordshire using a Shelbourne Reynolds attachment.

— **RIGHT**

Harvesting Millet

Lexion 430 cuts millet in October time, for Mr Patrick Wrixon of Devereux, Wootton Farm, Norton Canon in Herefordshire.

Millet has health food properties and is ground into flour as an alternative to wheat flour, it is also grown for bird seed. Buckwheat also has health food benefits and is commonly ground for flour.

— **BELOW RIGHT**

Harvesting Buckwheat

Some of the buckwheat grown at Devereux Wootton Norton Canon Herefordshire has also been used in wild bird seed mixes planted on the farm for the winter feeding of farmland birds, which is particularly welcome in the cold winter of 2009-2010.

— **BELOW**

Linseed

Lexion 570+Montana cuts linseed at the Hurst Morville, Bridgnorth, Shropshire. Linseed oil has valuable health benefits, omega 3 is found in cold pressed linseed oil. Oil is used in paints and varnish, animal feeds and as a treatment for leather.

UNCOUPLING AND ATTACHING HEADERS

With modern combines, uncoupling and fitting headers is a quick job. There are two lugs on the feed elevator, which fit into the brackets on the header. As the elevator with hydraulic rams is lifted, the header hangs on the lugs, and is attached into the brackets on the header, before the hydraulic couplings and pto shaft are attached. A lever is pulled to lock the header and large pins are inserted into the matching holes for them on the elevator, locking header and combine feed elevator together.

Headers

RAPE EXTENSION

Rape tangles as it grows, so the vertical rape knife parts the tangles by cutting through them, avoiding tangles with the reel, which is raised up out of work for cutting rape. The vertical knife can be driven electrically or hydraulically and it is fitted as an accessory together with filler plates as on a Claas combine with the Vario header extended to its furthest position.

— TOP RIGHT

OSR extension on Lexion 580+ with knife drive on V1200 Header.

— BOTTOM

Drago header.

— CENTRE

Biso header.

The header has a light non vibrating cast aluminium frame.

Made by Biso Schrattenecker of Austria and imported to the UK by Abrey Agricultural, Biso offer various headers to fit all makes of combine, including this Vario Alu-Ultralight 800 header, which differs from standard engineering in that it is built from modular cast aluminium sections, which is very much lighter. It also has a fully variable cutting bed which extends up to 800mm. The auger is

stainless steel, which is split in the middle while the dual knives overlap for efficient operation across the 12m cut. Being made of aluminium and toughened plastic means that the weight is considerably less than conventional headers, down to 4 tons on a 12ft header. Rather than being split centrally directly in front of the driver , the reel is split off centre to the left, giving better visibility from the cab, so there is less obstruction to the drives view of the intake area.

Biso also make a Universal Crop Ranger header and extensions for rape seed, the Biso Integral CX, and soya bean harvesting called a Biso Soja-Flex.

— BOTTOM RIGHT

Claas Vario V1200.

This header has been redesigned, rather than an add-on to existing V10.50 header. Robust Gearboxes and shafts largely replace chains and belts, and linear knife gearboxes on each side of the header, drive the twin knives. They also drive a pump on the near side that works vertical knives for rape. The knife is in two halves on this V1200 header, driven by eccentric planetary gears from either side, rather than the conventional wobble boxes. Stroke rate has increased from 1.120/min to 1,334/min. The intake auger is also split

in two and is 660mm diameter instead of the 580mm, to improve capacity.

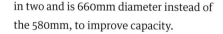

— **RIGHT**

Many combines find new owners through retirement sales or sales due to changes in farming policy. This Dominator 118SL Maxi changed hands at Ellenhall Park Farm, Eccleshall, Near Stafford in May 2009, sold by Bagshaws auctioneers of Bakewell, and was sold to a dealer for export for £17,000.

— **BOTTOM**

Many combines change hands at collective machinery sales such as this one at Hazel Meadows Ledbury. This Lexion 510 was sold to a used machinery dealer for £67,000.

The machine was for sale as a result of a local contractor retiring, at a Collective machinery sale held by H J Pugh of Ledbury, Herefordshire, a firm which was established in 1990, and is specialised in handling sales of vintage and modern machinery.

Export

JMT Engineering (Ladbrooke) Ltd. Bishops Itchington, Southam, Warwickshire

Many used combines are being exported and while this deprives the UK market it does save some from an early death, as the recent surge in metal prices is providing an incentive to scrap older machines. Some dealers selling new combines have always exported the trade in used combines, but this has increased during the last five years. Eastern European countries are improving their farms with increased mechanisation so there is a ready market for these second hand combines. Newer combines such as CSX models form New Holland are sent to France and Germany, but Bulgaria was also a major importer recently. One dealer sends models abroad from the Dominator series to the latest Lexions. Another used machinery dealer specialising in tractors and combines in the UK exports to Russia, Ukraine, Poland Lithuania, Latvia and Poland, dealing in all harvesters across the range from the 1970's to the 2000's. There has been an increased demand from the Baltic States while older machines tend to go to the more distant countries, such as Pakistan, Malaysia and Thailand. The NH 8000 series are particularly popular with Pakistan buyers. There are now two main scrap yards left in the UK, dealing in older combines, where some are sent abroad.

The current value of the Euro as at 2009 is helping the export trade and with labour in countries such as Pakistan and Poland being so much cheaper than in the UK and the cost of parts for all makes being expensive here, it is more economical to export machines than to re-condition them here. John Deere harvesters, such as the more recent WTS and STS models are popular in Scandinavia, as are New Holland TX66 and the older 8060 and 8080 models. One of the largest exporters of farm machinery from the UK exports world wide as there is a ready market for all makes and models of machinery.

— **THIS PAGE**
A New Holland 8030 is dismantled for export to Pakistan.

Swathing or Chopping

Until it was finally prohibited by law, straw burning was a quick and effective way of disposing of unwanted surplus straw, and preparing fields for the next crop after harvest. After the ban on burning, straw choppers became very common. When the straw chopper is moved forward out of work, the combine is set for swathing, and straw can be discharged in rows on the stubble. Material such as husks, chaff and other light material blown off the sieves is distributed by the chaff spreader on many combines.

— **ABOVE**

Lexion 530 in OSR chopping the rape atHaulm Bitterley Ludlow Shropshire.

— **LEFT**

Barley Straw in swath rows.

Fires

— Main Image
This Lexion 580+TT met a premature end to her life, burnt out after only a year's work, barely weeks after leaving the workshop at the dealers, this Lexion 580+TT was half way through its second harvest when it caught fire. Its destiny is now the breakers yard JMT Engineering (Ladbrook) Ltd, Southam, Warwickshire. The cause was not completely established but a hydraulic hose may have broken with oil spraying on to the hot engine. Fire is a big hazard to combines and many of all makes have met an untimely end to their life through fire damage.

Many older machines as well as those damaged by fire end their days in the breakers yard.

JMT Engineering (Ladbroke) Ltd, is one of these centres who also buy and sell all makes and models of combines and supply parts for Claas, John Deere, Massey-Ferguson, New Holland and other makes. Parts salvaged from combines in the breakers yard keep other machines going.

— Centre Right
Dominator damaged by fire at JMT Engineering Ltd.

— Top Right
Lexion 580 damaged by fire sold, by Mill. Engineers ended its days at a salvage yard

Fire damaged combines are frequently found in salvage and scrap yards. Overheating was always a problem with combine engines, which was often caused by the radiator clogging with dust and chaff. The rotary filters were fitted to help prevent this, but they can still get blocked.

The Rotary filters have an internal rotating arrangement that blocks part of the filter while brushing out any rubbish attached, most of which drops clear, leaving plenty of clear filter to admit cooling air. Cleaning combine radiators and filters is essential to avoid any fire risk.

End of their life - Signs of progress

These older combines now robbed of their parts are broken up for scrap at Morris Corfield & Co Ltd, in order to make way for new and more modern combines at their new headquarters at Benthall, Shropshire.

— **BELOW LEFT**

Senators at the end of their life await the arm of the metal cutting device and the scrap merchant.

— **BELOW RIGHT**

Dominator 85 in scrapyard at back of dealers.

— **BOTTOM RIGHT**

MF 625 in breakers yard at JMT Engineering (Ladbrooke Ltd), Southam, Warwickshire.

— **BOTTOM LEFT**

At the hands of the breakers cutting knife, contractor Frank Breakwell of Telford and a Hyundai digger with cutting knife cuts up an old Dominator 100.